Manufacturing

GCSE

Steve Wallis
Neil Godfrey

Published in 2005 by:
Nelson Thornes Ltd
Delta Place
27 Bath Road
CHELTENHAM
GL53 7TH
United Kingdom

05 06 07 08 09 / 10 9 8 7 6 5 4 3 2 1

A catalogue record for this book is available from the British Library.

ISBN 0-7487-9374-7

Page make-up by GreenGate Publishing Services, Tonbridge, Kent

Printed in Great Britain by Scotprint

To the memory of Bill Taylor

Acknowledgements   iv

Introduction   vii

UNIT 1   2
Designing Products for Manufacture

Design briefs   4

Design specification and solutions   7

The selection of materials   22

Developing design ideas   31

Getting started on presenting your design solution   56

Completing your design portfolio   73

UNIT 2   84
Manufactured Products

Production plans and schedules for manufacture   86

Resource requirements   97

The stages of production   101

Teamwork and team building   124

Preparation for manufacture   139

Manufacturing processes   141

Focus on paper and card production   165

Focus on the printing and publishing industry   177

Focus on the textile industry   191

Focus on the pharmaceutical industry   206

Focus on the food manufacturing industry   212

Health and safety   216

Applying quality and production control techniques   221

UNIT 3   240
Application of Technology

The manufacturing and engineering sectors   242

The use of information and communications technology   248

New materials and components   273

Systems and control technology   287

The application of technology   301

Exam hints   318

Revision questions   319

Index   322

Acknowledgements

The Authors would like to thanks the following friends and colleagues for their kind help and support in the writing of this book:

Richard Peacock, Keith Bradley, Mark Elliott and Anthony Carey for their excellent technical assistance and design work.

Special thanks to Darren Wallis for his valuable insight into the pharmaceutical industry, Chris Purnell at Nissan UK, Roy Kelly at North East Press Ltd and Carol Wilkinson at KP Foods.

Finally, special thanks also to Tom Guy at Greengate Publishing and Carolyn Lee at Nelson Thornes.

The authors and publisher would like to thank the following for the use of copyright material:

- 3T RPD Ltd, p. viii right, p. 31, p. 34, p. 46 top, bottom, p. 47 bottom, p. 48 right
- Adobe, p. 249
- Armax, p. 288, p. 289 left
- Assocation of the British Pharmaceutical Industry (ABPI), p. 206 middle
- Autodesk, p. 248 left, p. 251, p. 252 top
- Aylesford Newsprint Ltd, p. viii, p. 165
- Baird & Co, p. 24
- The Big Sheep, p. 192 bottom
- J. Braithwaite & Co (Sewing Machines Ltd), p. 204
- BSI Group, p. 51
- Bulmer & Lumb, p. 193 right
- Butterworth-Heinemann, p. 31
- CI Logistics, p. 289 right
- Cookson Bullion, p. 146
- Corbis/Bettmann, p. 34 top left
- Corbis/Royalty Free, p. 277
- Denford Ltd, p. 255 right, p. 271
- Digital Stock 7, cover
- Dyson, p. 47 top
- Epson, p. 189 second bottom

- Eyewire DT, cover
- Ford Motor Company Limited, p.10, p. 222 bottom
- Getty Images, p. 126 bottom
- GlaxoSmithKline, p. 209 top
- GreenGate Publishing, p. 10 bottom, p. 11, p. 12, p. 19, p. 21 top, middle, bottom, p. 23, p. 42, p. 52 bottom, p. 57 top, bottom left, bottom right, bottom far right, p. 86 top, p. 142 top left, p. 145 top, p. 152 bottom, p. 167, p. 168 top, bottom, p. 169 top, p. 171, p. 172 top, bottom, p. 175, p.178 . p. 179, p. 185 top, bottom, p. 187, p. 189 second top, p. 191, p. 192 top, p. 193 left, p. 197, p. 201 top right, p. 202, p. 218 top left, p. 223 top, p. 243 top, bottom, p. 244 top, p. 278, p. 279, p. 312, p. 314
- Harris Walton Lifting Gear Ltd, p. 152 top
- Hewlett-Packard Development Company, p. 244 bottom
- Highland Spring, p. 310
- Hodder Headline, p. 43
- Ideabook, www.ideabook.com, p. 10 top
- Image DJ vol 50 (High Tech World), p. 142 top right
- Image DJ vol 51 (Today's Communication), p. 57 bottom far left
- Image DJ vol 60 (Computer World), p. 48 top left, p. 127, p. 189 top, p. 207, p. 211 top right, p. 285
- Image DJ vol 65 (Machinery) p. 255 left
- Independent Forgings & Alloys Ltd., p viii, p. 151
- Institute of Operations Management (IOM), p. 88
- Juran Institute, Inc., p. 230
- KDO International West Ltd, p. 188
- M real UK Ltd, p. 169 bottom right, p. 180, p. 183 middle
- Manesty, p. 209 bottom
- Middlesex University Teaching Resources, p. 281, p. 282 right, p. 283
- Minitab, p. 238
- MRT Castings Ltd, p. 143 left, p. 148, p. 150
- National Grid Transco plc, p. 244 middle
- Nissan, p. xi left, p. 152 middle, p. 291, p. 295, p. 297
- NMSI, p. 206 bottom
- Nokia, p. 226
- Nova Development Corporation, p. vii left, right, p. 12, p. 34 top right, p. 52 top, p. 124, p. 126 top, p. 169

Introduction

You are almost certainly familiar with the latest telecommunications technology, such as the rapid development of mobile phones.

You are likely to have seen developments in digital music, vision and photography, for example, MP3 players, plasma-screen televisions and digital cameras. Likewise, leading manufacturers such as Sony, Phillips, Samsung, Panasonic and Sharp are generally well known household brand names.

You have probably watched your favourite sportsperson advertising their sponsored sportswear company or a brand of soft drink on television. David Beckham, Kelly Holmes, Jonny Wilkinson and Tim Henman all feature prominently in advertising campaigns.

At some point you will have seen the latest cars in magazines, or seen them in television programmes such as Top Gear.

At some point you may have consumed soft drinks such as Pepsi or Coca-Cola, eaten fast food such as that produced by McDonalds, Burger King or KFC, and used many of the household products you see advertised so often in the media.

You may be aware of these products because of marketing and advertising campaigns – the more effective these campaigns, the more familiar the products. It's natural to associate these products with their advertising campaigns, which is why companies spend billions of pounds a year on marketing, advertising and sponsoring top sportspeople, movie actors and pop stars.

Even though these advertisements can often be very striking, the really impressive part is in the manufacture of the products. Features of the manufacturing industry include:

- high specification computers, used in design and development, which can produce advanced 3D models to illustrate graphically virtual products
- advanced robotics and control systems used in processing and production
- new modern and smart materials developed specifically to improve products.

Without manufacturing you would not have the basic everyday things you require to function – no food, clothes, medicine, toiletries, never mind luxury items such as electrical goods.

Manufacturing keeps a large proportion of the world's population clothed, fed, clean and healthy: industries are able to produce billions of products each day.

Advertising may be a useful tool for selling, but manufacturing is where it really happens. Welcome to a whole new world!

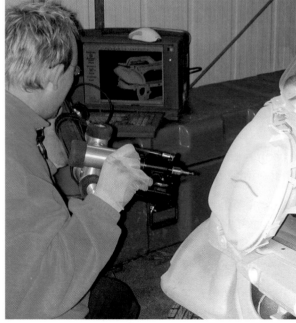

How this book is organised

This book will focus on three important aspects of engineering you have to study according to the specification. They are:

- Designing Products for Manufacture
- Manufactured Products
- Application of Technology

Jargon Dragons

Jargon Dragons are used in each unit to define some important terms, words and phrases which may be unfamiliar to you, but are important to understand in manufacturing.

Activities

Short exercises are used throughout this book to help you understand many important themes and subjects. The majority of the exercises are designed for you to carry out; however, you may sometimes require assistance from your teacher/lecturer.

Case studies

Case studies outline how real manufacturing and engineering companies produce products using the methods discussed in this book.

Find it out

This feature involves research topics and key points to investigate, to enable you to further understand the content.

Think it through

The 'think it through' feature is designed for you to develop your research skills with Units 1 and 2 and to help to revise key points within each unit.

What's in this unit?

To complete this unit you will need to design and develop a product, and to present your proposed design solution.

You will learn about customer design briefs, how to generate a product specification, including the key features, and investigate how production and material constraints can influence the final design choice.

You will learn how to use a range of drawing, design and graphical communications techniques, and be able to identify the best methods to help you present your chosen design solution.

In this unit you will also be introduced to methods of evaluating and testing your design, to ensure it meets fully the intended design brief.

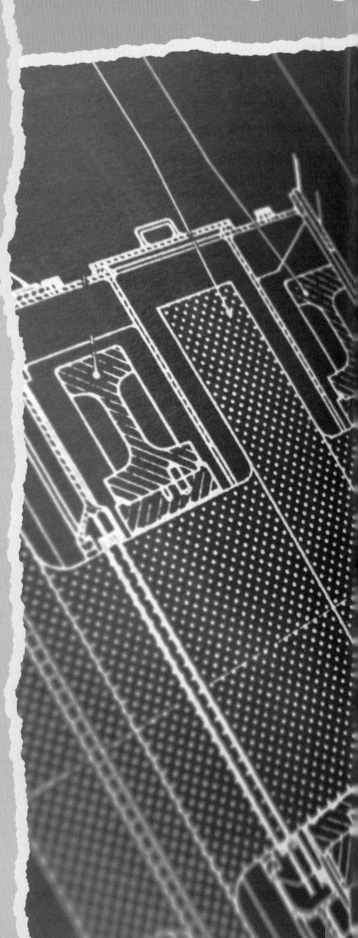

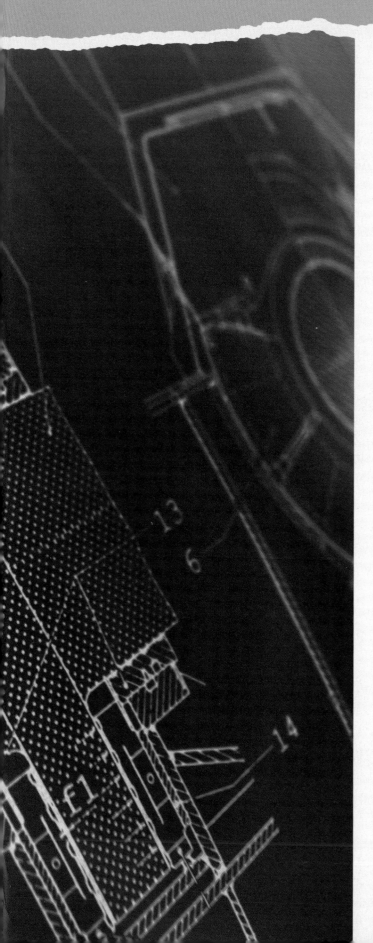

Products for Manufacture

1

In this unit you will learn about:

Design briefs	4
Design specification and solutions	7
The selection of materials	22
Developing design ideas	31
Getting started on presenting your design solution	56
Completing your design portfolio	73

Design briefs

A **design brief** is a basic description of what the customer or client wants. A client can be a customer, a friend or anyone who asks a designer to produce a design.

In business, commerce or industry, a company that requires a new design will approach a designer. The company will either employ the designer or use a specialist design company.

The design brief is an outline of what the client is looking for. It summarises the background to a problem and why the problem needs to be solved. Alternatively it may highlight the potential for improving an existing product.

The design brief generally includes references to key features, i.e. those features that are of primary concern to the intended customer. These important factors are:

- function
- quality standards
- performance
- intended markets
- size
- maintenance
- production methods
- cost
- regulations
- scale of production.

Function

The designer needs to answer the following questions:

- What will the product be used for?
- Where will it be used?
- Who will use it?
- How will they use it?

Quality standards
The designer will need to consider all the relevant standards that relate to the new product. Most products have to be designed

to meet standards of one sort or another. These may refer to the physical characteristics of the product or to its safety.

Performance
Performance is related closely to function. The designer will need to consider how well the product will do the task and how long the product will need to last.

Intended market
The product will be aimed at a particular group of customers. The designer will need to define this group of customers (the market), and to consider their wants and needs so that the new product will appeal to them.

Size
The designer will need to consider the size of the product. Sometimes, a small size is an important element of design – consider an engagement ring or other item of jewellery. Sometimes, being large is desirable to convey an impression of value, such as a car or a house.

Maintenance
Products do not last forever. Products need to be serviced, fixed or have their components changed from time to time. This process is known as maintenance. The designer will therefore need to consider how the product will be maintained.

Production methods
The production method will determine some aspects of the design. The designer will need to understand a range of production methods, as well as how designs are affected by these methods.

A company often already has particular types of machine which may need to be utilised. Sometimes the product may be designed first, and then the manufacturing process found to suit the design.

Production and processing are discussed in more detail within Unit 2: Manufactured Products.

Cost
In modern markets, there is strong competition between companies that produce similar products. In order to sell a product, it needs to be made as cost-effectively as possible. Some products demand low costs such as packaging or food products.

For some expensive products, cost is less important because they give the customer a feeling of status: common examples are mobile phones, training shoes, DVD players and plasma-screen TVs.

Think
IT THROUGH

When customers need a product, they want to pay as little as possible. However, when we really want a product, the price is not as important. Can you think of examples?

?

Regulations

Most products have been designed to meet guidelines. These could include legal obligations, restrictions on use of materials, or safety regulations such as age restrictions.

Scale of production

The design of the product will be influenced by the scale of production. The product may be a one-off product, or may be mass-produced. This feature is closely related to the production method.

The following descriptions of key features are all mixed up – simply match up the key feature with the correct description:

Key feature	Description
Regulations	The group of consumers for whom the design is being produced.
Scale of production	What the product will be used for, who will use it and how.
Maintenance	How well the product will do the intended task and how long it will last.
Performance	Legal obligations that the product must adhere to.
Intended market	The capacity of a product to be serviced and repaired.
Function	The size and amount of product being manufactured.

Answer on page 321

Design specification and solutions

When the designer has received the design brief from the customer, it is important to produce a design specification. The specification is a more complete list of requirements, which develops in more practical detail the key features highlighted within the design brief. In addition, designers will often consider other factors that were not discussed in our earlier list of key features.

Producing a design specification

There is no standard format for specifications but there are guidelines that should be followed.

The British Standard Institution has produced a document for product design specifications (PDS) entitled PD 6112: *A Guide to Preparation of Specifications.*

Product design specification key elements

The following list includes 29 elements contained within PD6112 and forms the core of the product design specification:

- aesthetics
- company
- competitors
- constraints
- cost of product
- customer
- documentation
- ease of disposal
- environment
- ergonomics
- installation
- legal
- life (shelf storage)
- life span of product
- maintenance
- manufacturing facility
- market constraints
- materials
- packing
- patents
- performance
- politics
- processes
- quality and reliability
- quantity
- safety
- shipping
- size
- standards.

As general guidance, a product specification could have the following sections:

- **title**
- **function**
- **client requirements**
- **design requirements**
  - physical and operational characteristics
  - safety
  - accuracy and reliability
  - life of service
  - shelf life
  - operating environment
  - ergonomics
  - size
  - weight
  - materials
  - aesthetics
- **production characteristics**
  - quantity
  - target product cost
- **miscellaneous**
  - customer
  - competition.

Once the design specification is complete, the designer has clear guidelines to work from. However, good designs will include further high quality investigation into all critical features.

Research and analysis techniques

It is always necessary in design to conduct some form of research – the simple reason is that designers don't know everything. Research should allow the designer to give due consideration to the key features while also refining design solutions. Generally the following methods provide useful information for research purposes.

Information from customers

This can take many forms; feedback might be obtained from:

- marketing surveys (questionnaires for example)

- feedback cards (sometimes found in CD cases), complaints and praise from customers (you may have noticed that popular magazines with a letters page normally have at least one letter saying how good the magazine is!)
- focus groups (groups of customers brought together to provide an honest appraisal of a product or service).

If you are designing a product for your portfolio, why not try out one of the above? An example feedback card is shown below.

Feedback card example

ABXZ Manufacturing Company

Please complete the details below and enter our free draw to win a new car.

Name: _____

Address: _____

_____

Which model did you purchase? _____

How much did it cost? _____

Did you like the choice of colours?

Did you like the styling? _____

Did you find the product value for money? ☐ Yes ☐ No

Would you recommend the product to a friend? ☐ Yes ☐ No

Please make any other comments that could help us improve this product:

_____

_____

Information from the Internet

The Internet is a great place to obtain information. It can be particularly useful when searching for information on manufacturing techniques, materials or design styles.

You can get some great design ideas at http://www.ideabook.com

Information from textbooks

You are obviously aware that textbooks can be helpful as a source of information, since you are reading this now.

An advantage of textbooks over the internet is that you do not need to trawl through irrelevant websites to find the information you need. Pick up a textbook on any specific subject and (as long as it has been written at the correct level) you will probably find pages of useful research.

Information from magazines and journals

Popular magazines are excellent for gauging current fashion styles, which can be extremely important for designers. Clothing, soft drinks, household electrical equipment and cars are all developed to accommodate technological, cultural and social changes in customer expectations.

These magazines contain a wide range of useful information for designers

If you are unsure how much change does take place, just think of an old pair of training shoes, a car with an old registration plate or a five-year-old computer – compare these older products to what is available in the shops right now.

An old model of a Ford Fiesta and the latest version

THE JARGON DRAGON

product life – how long a product is expected to last in the marketplace. Many products, such as clothing, tend have a limited product life as they are constantly developing to accommodate changing fashion trends. On the other hand, some popular food products such as Heinz Ketchup and Kellogg's Corn Flakes have comparatively long product lives stretching back many decades.

Periodic journals are often published by people with expertise in a particular area, such as engineering, computing or medicine. This type of publication can contain extremely useful information about what is happening in a particular vocational area, or developments that are expected in the future. As a designer, recognition of future changes that may affect your finished product are key to ensuring it has a good **product life**.

Product investigation

Product investigation is a useful tool in the manufacturing industry. It is very common (although rarely acknowledged) for competing manufacturing companies to buy each other's products and carefully take them apart, examining such features as the physical, material, processing, aesthetic and ergonomic properties.

The resulting intelligence can be used to improve their own products.

As a designer this is a good place to start. If possible, take a look at other existing products similar in purpose to your intended product.

A student carrying out an investigation

Quality function deployment

Quality function deployment (QFD) is a technique devised by a pioneer of modern-day quality – Joseph Juran. Juran is discussed a little later (within Unit 2: Manufactured Products), but for the moment we will take a quick look at the technique he designed to improve communication between the customer and the designer.

QFD is designed to take into account key considerations and combine them into a chart using symbols to illustrate how strongly they are linked or **correlated**.

The key considerations can be simplified as the voice of the customer and the voice of the manufacturing engineer, i.e. what the customer wants, and the technical considerations that affect the manufacturing process.

A customer consideration could be a desire for the product to be carried easily by hand; a corresponding technical consideration could be the weight and volume of material.

The two sets of considerations are placed in a chart which allows designers to draw links between what the customer wants and the technical requirements. A link can clearly be drawn between the portability of the product (customer) and the weight and volume of material (engineer). Designers can use such information to determine the most important aspects of the product and how best to allocate design time and focus.

> **THE JARGON DRAGON**
>
> correlation – how closely two or more features are related to each other. For example, the growth of grass in the summer may be positively correlated to the amount of rainfall.

Understanding the physical properties of a product

Any product interacting with us or with our environment will have a relationship with other products.

A product may need to be attached to, fit into, or stand on something – a simple coffee cup has a flat surface at the bottom so that it will stand on a table without falling over. The product may be part of a complex piece of equipment or machinery. It may need to function in a particular environment (some clothing is designed specifically for cold temperatures, such as that worn by astronauts in space).

It is necessary, therefore, to consider these external aspects when designing.

An astronaut's suit provides insulation

Example

A customer has approached a designer with the following brief.

A mobile phone holder is to be designed for use within an office environment. The holder must be able to accept a wide range of modern mobile phones. The handset must fit into the holder with the display screen visible at all times.

Data has been collected from a range of handsets:

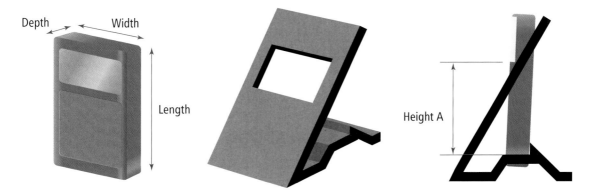

	Length (mm)	Height A (mm)	Width (mm)	Depth (mm)
Handset 1	120	50	35	19
Handset 2	110	40	35	17
Handset 3	65	30	32	22
Handset 4	80	35	37	23
Handset 5	80	34	32	17
Handset 6	75	33	34	19
Handset 7	100	42	40	17
Handset 8	85	40	32	16

Consider this range of mobile phones.

What size would you make the following characteristics?

Think
IT THROUGH

- *the height of the product*
- *the width of the pocket*
- *the depth of the pocket.*

In addition to the product's size, other physical characteristics include its volume, weight, mass and density.

Volume

This is a measure of how much space an object takes up, often expressed in cubic metres (m^3).

Example

A box with the dimensions of 2 metres wide × 3 metres long × 1 metre high will have a value of:

$$volume = width \times length \times height$$

$$= 2 \, m \times 3 \, m \times 1 \, m = 6 \, m^3$$

Volume becomes a little more difficult to calculate when discussing irregular or spherical shapes.

Mass

This is a measure of the amount of substance a product has, i.e. the amount of material used to make it.

Mass is measured in kilograms (kg).

Weight

Weight is often confused with mass. The weight of an object describes the gravitational force exerted on it by the Earth.

Weight is measured in newtons (N), named after the physicist and mathematician Sir Isaac Newton, who first came up with the concept of gravity – a common story is that he made this crucial discovery after observing an apple fall from a tree.

$$Weight = mass \text{ (in kg)} \times gravitational \ acceleration$$
$$(or \ gravity \ for \ short, \ in \ m/s^2).$$

On Earth, gravitational acceleration is equal to $9.81 \, m/s^2$. Therefore, an object with a mass of 1 kg, such as a bag of sugar, will have a weight of 9.81 N on Earth.

Note: Since the gravity on the Moon is roughly a sixth of that here on Earth, a bag of sugar will have a weight one-sixth of 9.81 N (1.64 N) on the Moon. Its mass, however will be the same – 1 kg – this is why you would weigh less on the Moon!

Density

If you packed one cardboard box with bricks, and another with feathers, which one do you think would be the most dense?

The box containing the bricks would obviously be more dense than the box containing the feathers.

The reason is that, although they occupy the same volume (or space), the bricks possess more mass. Density is calculated as follows:

$$\text{density} = \frac{\text{mass}}{\text{volume}}$$

Therefore, if the volume of the box was 1 m³ and the bricks had a mass of 25 kg, the feathers a mass of 0.4 kg:

$$\text{density of box with feathers} = \frac{0.4 \text{ kg}}{1 \text{ m}^3} = 0.4 \text{ kg/m}^3$$

$$\text{density of box with house bricks} = \frac{25 \text{ kg}}{1 \text{ m}^3} = 25 \text{ kg/m}^3$$

These boxes have exactly the same volume, but differ in mass, and therefore differ in weight and density

Understanding some basic scientific principles

When a product is designed, the designer has to realise that the product must be able to work in the 'real world', and must obey scientific rules.

The scientific rules that need to be considered can be extensive, and will depend largely on the type of product being designed. For example, the design of products for the biological industries has to take into account not only physical and material properties, but also chemical and microbiological principles.

Some common areas that may need to be considered are:

- components need to be supported
- levers and gears can magnify forces
- different types of force exist
- friction
- structures.

Components need to be supported
Consider the common kitchen stool below:

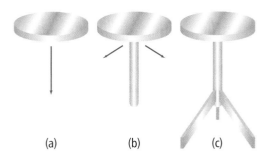

(a)   (b)   (c)

When the stool is being designed, the designer must take into account the following:

a The seat cannot float in the air. There is a constant force trying to push the seat towards the ground – this is the force of gravity. The seat must be supported by a force that is equal to the force of gravity, otherwise it would collapse. The material chosen must be strong enough to support this force.

b A vertical shaft has been added. This must be capable of supporting the seat and the person sitting on the stool. The design must also take into account variation in forces caused by a range of different-sized people sitting on the stool, and the sort of environment in which the stool will be used.

Centre of gravity has an important effect on stability. If the stool is unstable it will fall over – you don't need to be a rocket scientist to work that out!

The centre of gravity is a point through which the weight of the product acts, no matter which way it is rotated:

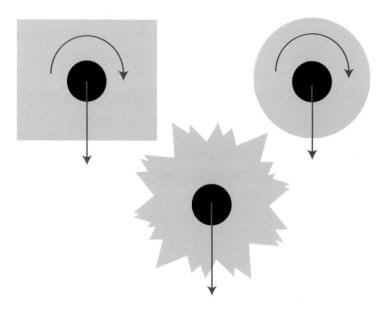

If the objects are rotated, the force acting down (weight) will always remain constant.

c So what has this to do with the stool? Consider the diagram on the next page. If the centre of gravity is over the base it is reasonably stable. However, when the centre of gravity moves past the base of the product, it becomes unstable, leading it to fall over. The centre of gravity must therefore be directly above the base of the stool. We have introduced three legs, which extend the base and make the stool more stable.

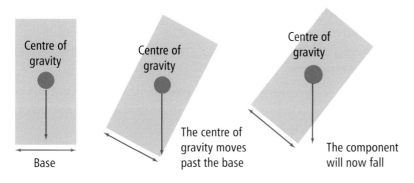

The stool is most stable when the centre of gravity is directly over the base

Forces

A force is an external energy applied to an object, often in the form of a push or pull. Forces are measured in newtons (N). We have already discussed one force – weight. One newton is equal to about 100 grams – about the same weight as a packet of super-noodles.

Forces can be classified into four types.

Tensile force	When a material is pulled or stretched
Compressive force	When a material is pushed or squashed
Torsional force	When a material is twisted
Shear force	When a material is cut or torn.

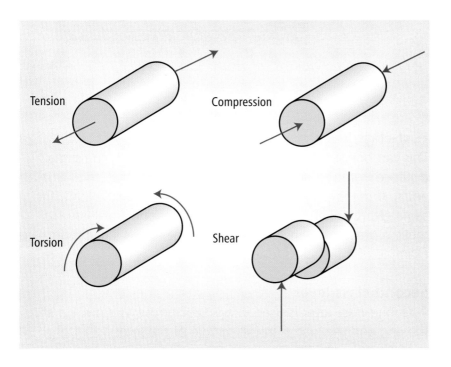

Different types of force

Components that are subject to forces can stretch, twist or deform. When designing a product, it is important to consider the strength of the material, and the size and geometry of the components being subjected to an external force.

Levers magnify forces

A well-known saying claims that if you 'build a lever long enough you can move the world', meaning that levers can be used to increase the size of the force being applied to an object. This is why burglars use crowbars to break into houses, or why people sometimes use long sticks to help move objects such as a car stuck in the mud.

There are three main types, or classes, of lever:

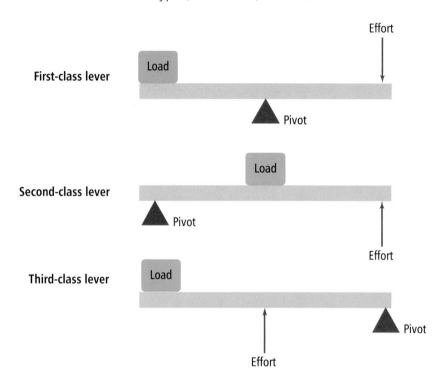

Different types of lever

First-class lever

This can be used to lift heavy loads. If the effort is the same distance from the pivot as the load, the effort and load remain equal. If the effort is further from the pivot than the load, the same effort will lift a heavier load, but the effort will have to move a greater distance. A children's see-saw is a common example of a first-class lever.

Second-class lever

A second-class lever is used in a wheelbarrow. The pivot is at the end and the load is in the middle of the lever.

Third-class lever

This lever has the load at one end and a pivot at the other end. The load is applied in the centre of the lever. Tweezers or barbecue tongs are both examples of third-class levers.

Where can levers be found on a mountain bike? Make sketches of all the levers. What classes of lever are there?

Think
IT THROUGH

Friction

If you kicked a football, hit a golf ball, or even closed this book and slid it across the table, each one would slow down and eventually come to rest.

The reason for this is friction.

Friction is a force between two surfaces in contact, acting in parallel to them, opposing or preventing their motion.

We use the coefficient of friction, μ (the Greek letter mu) to give us a value of friction which is based upon a scale of 0–1.

A very low coefficient would indicate a very small amount of friction (a snowboard on ice). A high coefficient would indicate two surfaces generating a lot of friction (a car tyre on tarmac).

Two materials are always stated when giving values of the coefficient of friction.

Sometimes components need to slide, whereas sometimes components need to almost stick with friction. It is important to consider friction when components are being designed to move, slide or rotate.

Some examples are shown in the table below. The word kinetic refers to movement in this instance:

Material	Coefficient of friction (kinetic)
Metal on metal (lubricated)	0.07
Wood on wood	0.3
Waxed wood on snow	0.05
Rubber on concrete (wet)	0.5
Rubber on concrete (dry)	0.7

The coefficient cannot be zero as it is impossible to have no friction. When designers are considering which materials to use they should always think about the effects of friction. Lubrication, such as the use of oil, drastically reduces friction by filling in imperfections in the surface texture.

When magnified the surface contains imperfections that can be described as 'peaks' and 'valleys'

The lubricating material fills in the imperfections ensuring a more consistent surface texture

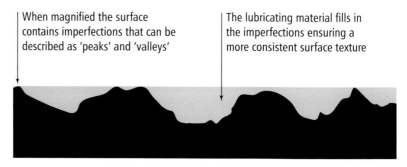

The effect of lubrication

Structures

Structures are designed to resist the forces applied to them.

A structure moves forces from one point to another so that the structure can withstand a force and remain stable.

Structures can be:

- solid
- frame
- shell.

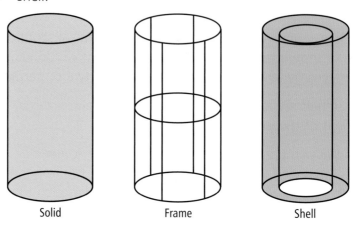

Different types of structure

Solid   Frame   Shell

Solid structures are used everywhere to offer support – if you are sat at a table on a chair, the legs are doing the support job right now. Shell structures are often used as containers or pipes – your water and gas pipes at home are shell-type structures used to support the water and gas that supply your drinking water and central heating.

Framed structures are used in the construction industry all the time – to build houses, colleges, office buildings, gas holders and bridges.

These structures use frames to redistribute forces. This type of structure can also be applied to many manufactured or engineered products.

The Millenium Bridge over the River Thames in London

A skyscraper in Canary Wharf, London

Gas holders

The selection of materials

Designers have an almost endless range of materials to choose from. One of the most important considerations to be made when designing a product is the choice of materials. It is therefore useful to understand the different categories so that it is possible to identify quickly the best material for the job.

But before we identify the groups of materials, the following points should be considered:

- **Service** – what does the product need to be able to do?
- **Properties** – what characteristics will the material need to have? Will it need to be strong? Is the weight an issue?
- **Environment** – what sort of surroundings will the product be used in?
- **Aesthetics** – what will the product look like? Is it important that it has a particular look, colour or feel?

In many cases different materials can be used for the same product. Other considerations are the cost and processing capabilities of the material, i.e. can it be formed, machined, cut, joined and finished to the appropriate standard.

Think IT THROUGH

Look at products that are similar but made from different materials, such as wood, metals, plastic or ceramics. Why have they been made from different materials?

Categories of materials

Materials used in design generally fall into one of the following categories:

- metals
- polymers
- ceramics
- composites
- wood, paper and board
- textiles.

Metals

Metals fall into two main categories: ferrous and non-ferrous.

Ferrous metal contains iron. Pure iron has some uses but is generally regarded as being too soft and ductile for most manufactured products. However, if a small amount of carbon is mixed with iron, there are many changes that take place in the material's properties.

Adding carbon to iron makes a new material known as steel. Carbon steels can be categorised into different types, depending on how much carbon is in the steel.

- 0.1–0.3% carbon = mild steel
- 0.3–0.7% carbon = medium carbon steel
- 0.7–1.3% carbon = high carbon steel.

Grey cast iron contains 94% iron, 3% carbon and small amounts of other elements. It is a hard material, but it melts relatively easily, so can be poured into moulds to make cast products. Cast iron can be machined quite easily after it has been moulded to produce the required finish.

Non-ferrous metals do not contain any iron. There are many non-ferrous metals, some of which are very common. You may already recognise some names such as copper or aluminium.

Let us look more closely at non-ferrous metals.

Aluminium

Aluminium is used where products are required to have little weight, such as in aeroplane components. mountain bike components, or foil for cans and ornaments.

It can easily be melted and moulded into shape and has excellent resistance to corrosion, hence its use in kitchen foil and drinking cans.

An aluminium can

Copper

Copper is dark orange in colour and is very commonly used throughout the world in water pipes and electrical cables. It is very ductile, which means that it can be stretched into very thin lines to make copper wire. It is excellent at conducting electricity and heat, and can be easily worked upon in the workshop, or pressed into shape by machines. It does not corrode easily, but the surface will oxidise over long periods of time.

These bars of gold are highly valuable

Precious metals

Metals such as gold, silver and platinum are very precious and are therefore very expensive. Although these metals are often used to make jewellery, they have other uses. For instance, gold and silver are extremely good at conducting electricity.

Alloys

When metals or elements are mixed together to form a new material the new mixture is known as an alloy.

Many alloys exist. Some are light alloys, such as zinc, aluminium and titanium alloys; others are heavy alloys, such as copper, lead and nickel alloys.

Brass

Brass is an alloy of copper and zinc. It has a relatively low melting point (800°C) and can be cast easily. Brass does not corrode easily and can be polished to a high gloss finish similar to that of gold. This means that it is very often used for ornamental or decorative furniture for indoor and outdoor use. Brass is best known for its use in musical instruments (trumpets, trombones, etc.) but is also extensively used for door handles, locks and keys.

Bronze

Bronze is an alloy of copper and tin. There are two main types:

- Gun metal, which is 88% copper, 10% tin and 2% zinc. It is relatively easy to machine and is corrosion resistant. It is used for marine components such as valves, pumps and steam fittings.
- Phosphor–bronzes can vary according to the quantities of each alloying metal. They also contain the chemical phosphorous. This material has excellent wear resistance and corrosion resistance, and is used to produce bearings.

Think it through

Think it through

Consider the following components. Try to select an appropriate metal for each. Remember, there could be more than one answer, so discuss your answers in small groups:

- *an outside door handle*
- *a mountain bike frame*
- *water pipes*
- *a drinking can.*

Think IT THROUGH

Polymers

Polymer is a scientific term used to describe plastics and rubber materials.

The first plastics were developed over 100 years ago, and, although they had limited uses initially, by the time of World War 2, many new applications had been found, such as in clothing.

Since that time designers have found thousands of uses for polymers; today we can see countless products made with polymers. Polymers are light and corrosion resistant, and can be processed in a variety of colours. Tooling or mould tools are needed to produce components from polymers; however, once the appropriate tooling has been produced component manufacture is a very quick and accurate process. This tooling is often very expensive.

An injection moulding machine can be used to form plastic moulded products. These machines are used in mass production and can sometimes take only a few seconds to produce complex components such as mobile phone covers.

Tools made of plastic

An injection moulding machine

There are many different types of polymers, which can be categorised into two main groups: thermosets and thermoplastics.

Thermosets

Thermosets are formed into shape using heat. When the shape is cooled, the component that has been produced cannot be re-shaped in the same way as thermoplastics. Thermoset polymers can withstand higher temperatures than thermoplastic polymers, and are used in products that are exposed to heat.

These products include many electrical components, such as switches and light fittings, and handles for products that give off heat, such as kettles, pans and irons, etc.

Thermoplastics

Thermoplastics can be reheated, allowing them to take a new shape when pressure is applied. If the product is reheated, the material can be re-shaped using pressure.

Some of the most popular polymers tend to be thermoplastics; some examples are described in a little more detail below.

ABS (acrylonitrile butadiene styrene)

This material has excellent resistance to impact. It is used to manufacture electrical cases, car parts, telephones, helmets and surfboards. If a product needs to be made accurately, but will be expected to take impacts in normal use, ABS is a suitable material.

PVC (polyvinyl chloride)

This is a very versatile material. In solid form it is strong and durable. It is used to make windows and conservatories as it can be extruded easily. It can be made soft with the additional of fillers and is often used as an alternative to leather.

PVC has excellent electrical resistance properties and is used as an insulator to cover electric cable.

Polystyrene

This material is hard and strong. It can be brittle in thin sections but has the advantage that it can be manufactured in a transparent or clear form. It is used as a safe form of glass substitute for items such as CD covers, boxes or pens. Polystyrene can also be expanded into a foam material, used for drinking cups and packaging.

Nylon

This material is very tough and has good wear resistance. It can be moulded very accurately, and is used for technical products such as gears and bearings.

Acrylic

This material is supplied in flat sheet form and often used as a safe alternative to glass. It is used for machine guards and boxes. It is often transparent but can be coloured.

The following tables may prove useful when selecting metals, polymers and wood materials. (Textiles, food and drink, and paper products are discussed in detail within Unit 2: Manufactured Products.)

Selecting metal materials

Material	Composition	Melting point/°C	Uses	Hardness	Strength	Ductility	Conductor	Resistance to wear	Resistant to corrosion	Can be welded	Can be formed	Can be machined
Aluminium	Pure	660	Cooking foil, drinks cans, aircraft parts, cooking utensils	Soft	Yes	Weak	Yes	Low	Yes	Yes	Yes	Yes
Brass	Copper and zinc	700	Door handles, ornaments, screws	Medium	Yes	Weak – Medium	Yes	Low	Yes	Yes	Yes	Yes
Cast iron	Iron and carbon (3.5%)	1200	Manhole covers, engine castings, vices	Hard	No	Strong	Yes	High	No	Yes	No	Yes
Copper	Pure	1100	Cables, pipes, printed circuit boards	Soft	Yes	Strong	Yes	Low	Yes	Yes	Yes	Yes
Gold	Pure	1063	Jewellery and electronics devices	Soft	Yes	Weak	Yes	Low	Yes	Yes	Yes	Yes
High carbon steel	Iron and carbon (0.8 – 1.4%)	1300	Hand tools such as hammers and chisels	Hard	No	Strong	Yes	High	No	Yes*	No	Yes
Lead	Pure	327	Used to make solder (along with tin), roof flashing and paint	Soft	Yes	Weak	Yes	Low	Yes	Yes	Yes	Yes
Medium carbon steel	Iron and carbon (0.3 – 0.7%)	1300	Car parts, hand tools, bike parts	Hard	Yes	Strong	Yes	High	No	Yes	Yes	Yes
Mild steel	Iron and carbon (0.15 – 0.35%)	1250	Screws, hand tools, car doors, filing cabinets	Soft	Yes	Medium	Yes	Low	No	Yes	Yes	Yes
Silver	Pure	962	Jewellery, surgical tools, coins, ornaments	Soft	Yes	Weak	Yes	Low	Yes	Yes	Yes	Yes
Stainless steel	Iron, carbon, chromium, manganese and nickel	1250	Kitchen utensils and sinks, car parts and bathroom taps	Hard	Yes	Strong	Yes	Yes	Yes	Yes	Yes	Yes
Tin	Pure	232	Used to make solder (along with lead) and as food cans	Soft	Yes	Weak	Yes	Low	Yes	Yes	Yes	Yes
Titanium	Pure	1668	Car parts and aircraft components	Hard	Yes	Strong	Yes	High	Yes	Yes	Yes	Yes
Zinc	Pure	400	Used to plate (galvanise) other metals	Soft	Yes	Weak	Yes	High	Yes	No	No	Yes

*(with care)

Selecting thermoplastic materials

Material	Thermoset or thermoplastic	Uses	Impact resistance	Hardness	Strength	Conductor	Resistance to corrosion	Can be extruded	Can be moulded	Can be machined	Can be welded
ABS	Plastic	Mobile phone casings, games consoles, car parts	High	Hard	Strong	No	Yes	Yes	Yes	Yes	Yes
Nylon	Plastic	Gears and bearings in electrical equipment, clothing	Low	Hard	Strong	No	Yes	Yes	Yes	Yes	Yes
HDPE	Plastic	Bottles, pipes, shower gel containers	Medium	Hard	Medium	No	Yes	Yes	Yes	Yes	Yes
LDPE	Plastic	Bottles, toys, bags	High	Soft	Weak	No	Yes	Yes	Yes	Yes	Yes
PVC	Plastic	Cable insulation, windows, toys, footballs	High	Soft	Weak	No	Yes	Yes	Yes	Yes	Yes
Polystyrene	Plastic	Foam packaging, cups, ceiling tiles, toys	Low	Hard	Weak	No	Yes	Yes	Yes	Yes	Yes

Selecting wood materials

Material	Hardwood/ softwood	Uses	Hardness	Strength	Conductor	Resistance to corrosion	Good finish	Can be machined
Ash	Hard	Cricket stumps, furniture, baseball bats, plywood	Hard	Strong	No	Poor	Yes	Yes
Balsa	Hard	Model making, water sports equipment	Soft	Weak	No	Poor	No	Yes
Beech	Hard	Flooring, furniture	Hard	Strong	No	Poor	Yes	Yes
Birch	Hard	Flooring, furniture, plywood	Hard	Strong	No	Poor	Yes	Yes
Mahogany	Hard	Flooring, furniture	Medium	Medium	No	Medium	Yes	Yes
Oak	Hard	Flooring, furniture	Hard	Strong	No	Medium	Yes	Yes
Pine	Soft	Outdoor and bedroom furniture, flooring	Soft	Weak	No	Medium	Yes	Yes

Joining

Joining is a process used to assemble two or more components together. Some common methods of joining are described below.

Threaded fasteners

Screws and bolts are metal fasteners which have excellent strength. Both components to be joined are drilled, and a bolt is placed in the resulting holes. A nut is fixed to the bolt and tightened – to apply enough force, a spanner or wrench is used.

Threaded fasteners are useful because they can be taken apart easily, and are cheap and effective.

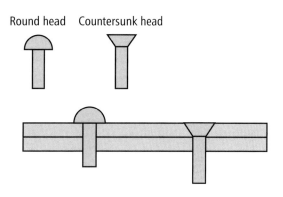

Round head   Countersunk head

Rivets

Rivets are similar to bolts but are not threaded. They are placed in a hole; the end of the rivet is then hammered over to form a dome or a flat surface. Rivets are not reversible. The process of removing them would cause damage. Rivets are used where the joint is expected to be permanent.

Soldering, brazing and welding

Metals can be joined by **non-fusion welding**.

These processes involves putting the two materials together and heating the metals to a specific temperature. When the materials are at the correct temperature, a filler is introduced. As the filler melts it fills the gap between the two materials and solidifies. The result is a solid, strong join.

Non-fusion welding – when the two pieces of metal to be welded do not melt. Only the filler material melts which holds the metals together.

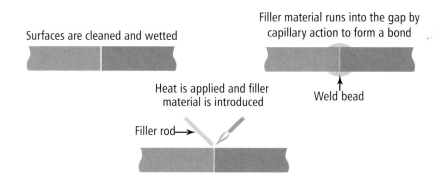

Surfaces are cleaned and wetted

Filler material runs into the gap by capillary action to form a bond

Heat is applied and filler material is introduced

Weld bead

Filler rod→

Soldering is used for materials with a melting point temperature below 450°C and brazing for material with a melting point above 450°C.

Fusion welding is used when the actual metals being joined are melted and form the filler. The joints made are permanent and waterproof. The process is mainly used for working with metals, although it is possible to weld plastics.

Nails

Nails are used to join wood. They are not strong enough to join steel, composites or ceramics and can fracture plastics. They often support other means of joining, such as gluing.

Wood joints

There are several different methods of joining wood. Common types of wood joints are lap, mitre, dovetail, and tongue and groove, shown in the diagram below:

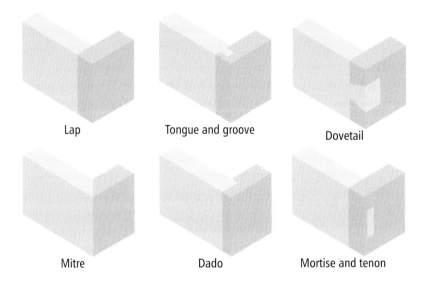

Lap   Tongue and groove   Dovetail

Mitre   Dado   Mortise and tenon

Different types of wood joint

Adhesives

The most important issue in using adhesives is choosing the correct type.

Woods can be joined with adhesives such as polyvinyl acetate (PVA) glue. Metal and ceramics require contact adhesives or epoxy resins.

The paper and publishing industries use glues frequently to bind products together – have a look at the spine of this book!

The surfaces of both materials being joined should be clean from dirt and grease to ensure a good contact is made. Adhesives can often be dangerous – users should always read the safety instructions on the packaging.

Sewing and stitching

In the textile industry the most common method of joining materials is the use of sewing or stitching techniques. Often highly automated, the process involves using a thread (often made of cotton), and a needle of some sort to secure the materials together.

Developing design ideas

By the time you arrive at the stage of developing your design ideas, you should have a good understanding of what the customer actually wants.

Remember that the customer could be anyone for whom the final product is intended – a company, your teacher, a friend or the general public could all be intended customers, depending on what you are designing.

Listening to the 'voice of the customer' is an essential factor when establishing the key features of your design – it has been suggested that a common reason for poor design is poor communication between the customer and the designer.

Design questions such as those listed below should have been considered by this stage of the design process.

Who did this lawnmower's designers listen to?

- What size, shape and weight should it have?
- What physical characteristics are important (taste, smell, sound)?
- How strong should it be?
- How will temperature and humidity affect it?
- Is reliability important?
- Is ease of carrying an issue?
- Are there any legal requirements or standards to be considered?
- Are there any safety requirements?
- Does it need power and will it consume energy; if so, what type (mechanical, electrical, hydraulic etc.)?
- Will it pollute the environment in any way?
- How long should it last, what will break it and what happens if it breaks?
- What should it be made of?
- What aesthetics are important (what should it look like and who should it appeal to)?
- Are ergonomics important (how does it interact with human physiology)?
- Is fashion important? Does the product follow any trends or social/cultural styles?

(Adapted from *Design Engineering*, Cather *et al.*, 2001, Butterworth-Heinemann)

Generating design ideas

The design specification gives all the guidelines for the solution, and an outline of what is to be achieved by the product.

Some people find it very difficult to come up with ideas – this is quite normal.

The finished design is often changed and modified beyond recognition from the first thoughts of the designer.

Designers can use a mind mapping session to generate ideas.

For example, the following **mind mapping** exercise led to the design of a guitar stand:

THE JARGON DRAGON

mind mapping – a way of graphically representing ideas and linking them together

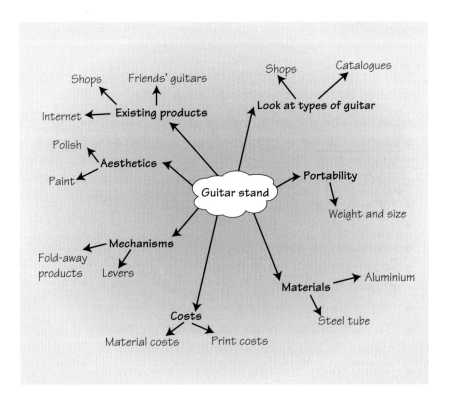

Look around

When you are designing a new product, look at a range of other products.

They may not be the same products but they may help you generate ideas. Look at things with no relevance at all to your chosen design for inspiration. For instance, many naturally occurring plants and animals are fantastically structured. Spiders' webs are an excellent example. Birds' nests are great assemblies, made without fasteners or adhesives, and many animals have brilliantly coloured and patterned skin or fur.

Sketch

Make notes and sketches of anything you think may be of help.
Here is a mind map of products with similar attributes to a
guitar stand.

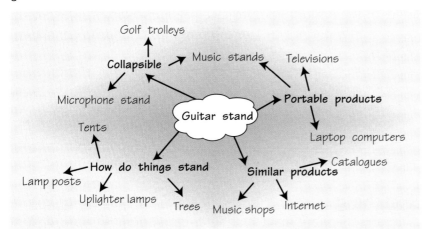

Here are some quick sketches based upon ideas from the mind
map.

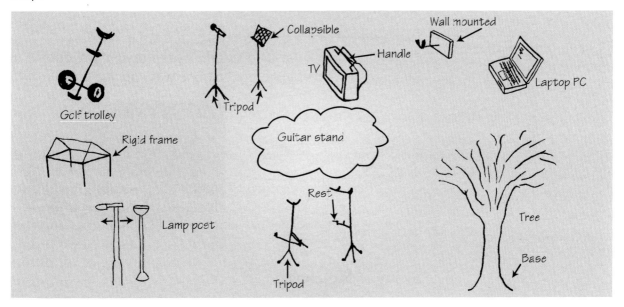

Notes are commonly included in sketches to remind the
designer of important features.

When generating ideas and creating mind maps remember:

- put down any ideas that come into your head
- do not leave ideas out because they do not sound very
  good
- the more ideas the better.

You can always eliminate the ideas if you decide not to use
them this time around.

Choosing from a range of designs

You will need to produce a range of designs from which to select a final design. This is better than producing only one design.

Many of the designs you produce will immediately be rejected because they are not suitable. The numbers of ideas generated could be:

General ideas	10–25	Sketches and notes
Good ideas	6–10	Concept drawings
Design sketch	3–4	Detailed concept drawings (or design sketches)
Final product	1	Technical drawings

Sketching

Although there are many computer-based drawing packages about it is still very important to use sketches. If you have a vision in your mind the best way to express it is by drawing it on some paper.

Leonardo Da Vinci's pioneering sketches are famous for capturing his thoughts and visions; he sketched a helicopter hundreds of years before the first one was engineered.

Da Vinci's helicopter sketch and a modern day helicopter

Example sketches

Here we see some example sketches of different products.

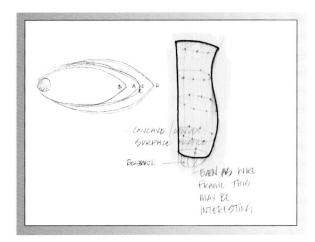

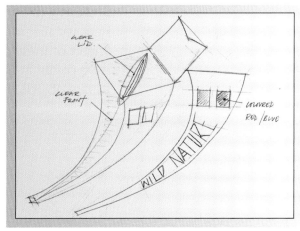

The use of shading

Shading is often used in sketching to bring an object to life by indicating a source of light, or the surface texture of a material.

A simple example is the shading of a cube.

Two-tone shading shows how light affects different sides of the cube, while three-tone shading includes the top surface.

When drawing using a drawing software package such as Paint or Paint Shop Pro it is possible to fill areas. This reduces the need for pencil shading and gives a professional look to a drawing.

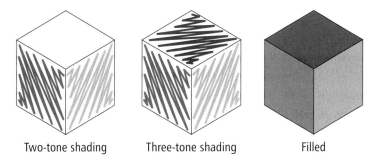

| Two-tone shading | Three-tone shading | Filled |

Shading cylindrical shapes

The same principle can be applied to round or cylindrical objects. In the diagram below, the red arrows show where the light is coming from.

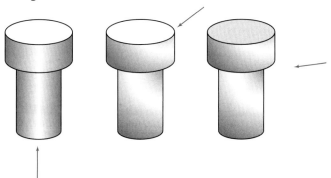

Shading drawings

Here we see simple shading. The light is the most important aspect of these drawings. Where the light hits the object there is no colour at all. These shapes are more difficult to shade than square objects, but shading can really show the object's form.

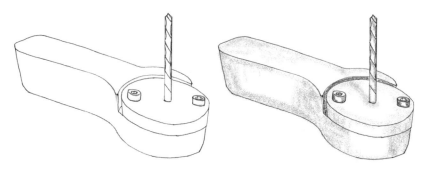

Shading can give a feeling of depth to a sketch

The product above has been sketched and has been shaded to give a real feeling of depth to it. If you look closely you will see that the product appears to have a shadow.

The fill facility on a graphics package blocks out the product with colour.

This can give a clear vision of what the product should look like. It is very easy to change colours, which is useful where surfaces require a finishing process such as painting.

The black and white sketch of a sports bag below has a few colours applied using a simple computer package, providing a feeling of warmth.

A sports bag before and after colour is added

Tips for sketching

When sketching try to follow these general guides:

- pick a view that shows as many of the subject's sides, edges and other features as possible
- draw the subject in 3D, use shading to indicate a light source
- by all means add colour, but use only a few shades of one or two colours, as really bright designs can sometimes be a little confusing to the viewer
- add text to highlight key features – try to keep the text short and to the point
- include a border and a title block with information such as the name of person who has drawn the sketch, the date and the title of the sketch.

Perspective drawing

Perspective drawing is often used by architects, artists and graphic designers, and can be a useful tool when presenting a design idea. It is usually applied to objects or landscapes when the artist is trying to convey space or distance.

Perspective drawings tend to be easy to understand, quick and cheap to produce and can make a product look more 'real' because it is how we see naturally.

This type of drawing works by focusing on a vanishing point within the drawing that is used as a reference point (the vanishing point is simply the point where objects become 'out of sight').

The most common types of perspective drawing are one-point and two-point perspective.

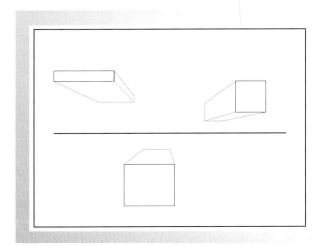

One-point perspective

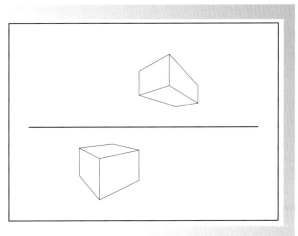

Two-point perspective

Generating concept designs

Put simply, concept designs are sketches used to show a design solution. Designers usually produce a number of concepts from which they will select the best. This decision depends on the relevance to the original brief and product specification, material and production constraints and most importantly feedback from the customer.

Example: bracket design

A simple bracket is to be designed to support a shelf within a computer desk. The designer sketches some basic shapes and ideas. These concept drawings are basic and show only the general idea of the proposed product. They provide the designer with a range of products to evaluate and choose from.

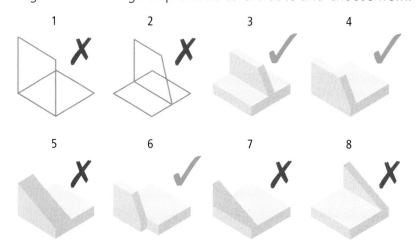

Concept drawings

Shortlist of proposed drawings

As you can see, designers may need to have lots of ideas in order to select one final product:

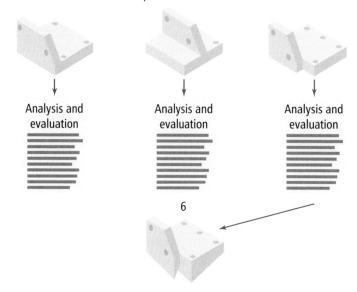

The process of analysis and evaluation leads to a final choice

The final three concepts are drawn in more detail and evaluated against the design specification.

A final product is chosen, based upon how well the product meets the design specification.

There should be about three good designs that could be seen as good solutions. This is known as a shortlist of design solutions.

At this stage the drawings are still known as concept designs. They do not have manufacturing details such as material and processing constraints, assembly techniques, joining methods or finish details. This is the next stage … .

Evaluation

Evaluation is a way of constantly checking to see if what you have designed meets the design specification. It is important to evaluate your work on an ongoing basis. Do not wait until the end, as too many important things may have changed.

Choosing your design solution

By now you should have the completed the following stages:

- received a design brief
- generated a design specification
- conducted relevant research
- sketched out your initial ideas as concept designs.

The next stage sounds simple – choose the design solution you think is the best. In fact, the decision making process can be quite difficult. Remember that poor design can sometimes result from not fully understanding the materials and processes involved.

To help you, consider the following points:

How will the product be manufactured?

To help you answer this question, consider whether any special tools or equipment are required. Will you have to be trained or highly skilled to use these tools and equipment? Think about what the product will look like at the end of the process and consider the material properties – is it possible to process the material using the method you have chosen? Consideration must also be given to the assembly and finishing processes. How will the components be joined? Will the process be automated? What type of finish will be used? Will the finish provide adequate protection from environmental effects such as surface corrosion?

What is the cost?

Consider the material and manufacturing costs of your design – sometimes a cheaper material or process might function as well and therefore prove more economical.

What material is to be used?

The most important part of any product is the material chosen. Ensure that the material, once processed, will function and look as you have designed it. Consider the weight, shape, feel and look of the material in addition to physical properties such as ductility and strength.

What quality and finish is required?

Think about the finished look and feel; what quality standards are you working to and are there any tolerances or constraints in place? Most importantly, think about how the product will perform once in use, and above all, consider what the customer will want!

Remember always:
The design specification is the main list of guidelines you will need to look at in relation to the key features.

Key features:
- function
- quality standards
- performance
- intended markets
- size
- maintenance
- production methods
- cost
- regulations.

The design sketch

The design sketch is the conclusion of the process that started with the generation of a design solution (or concept). It should briefly answer all of the questions previously asked in this section, and be presented in a neat, professional manner.

It will contain a sketch of the product, rough dimensions, material and processing considerations, in addition to comments regarding quality and finish.

An example is shown below:

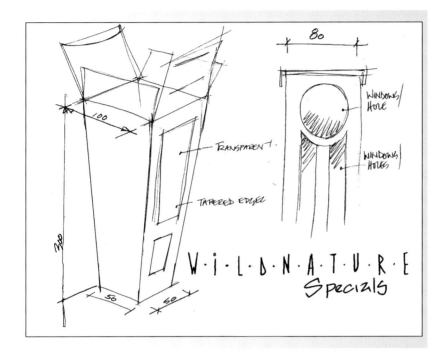

A design sketch of a flower box

Following the completion of a design sketch, designers can start the process of producing technical drawings that will eventually lead to the first prototype of the product being designed.

Technical drawing

Technical drawings are a fundamental part of manufacturing industry. The chances are that a technical drawing, of some type, has been used to make any given product.

Technical drawings are detailed, accurate and specific documents that are used by industry personnel to cover almost all manufacturing-based operations. Technical drawings are used for costing and quoting, production planning, processing, maintenance, assembly and quality assurance.

The main types of technical drawings used in industry are:

- orthographic projection
- pictorial drawing
- assembly drawing
- exploded drawing.

Orthographic projection

Orthographic projection is a commonly used method for producing drawings for products that have very accurate features and dimensions.

Despite being presented in 2D, this technique displays the product from different views so that features, such as sides, edges and holes, are visible to the viewer.

Orthographic projection can sound a little daunting at first. However, once introduced, it is a relatively straightforward way of representing design objects.

There are two forms of orthographic projection:

- first-angle is used in the UK and Europe
- third-angle is used in the US.

The differences are shown below:

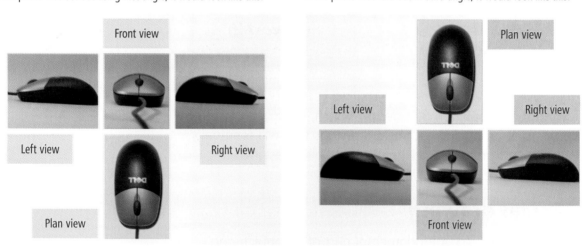

If the photo was set out using first angle, it would look like this:

Front view
Left view
Right view
Plan view

If the photo was laid out in third angle, it would look like this:

Plan view
Left view
Right view
Front view

Turn to page 67 for a quick guide to producing orthographic drawings.

Pictorial drawing

Pictorial drawings (along with orthographic projection) are classed as technical drawings, despite showing a component in 3D instead of 2D.

The advantage of a pictorial view over an orthographic view is that what the drawing represents is immediately obvious. Pictorial drawings can therefore be used to show an object in a more graphical and understandable way.

There are different methods of pictorial drawing. The two most popular are:

- isometric drawing
- oblique drawing.

Isometric drawing

Isometric drawings are used to display an object in 3D, using three main base lines (sometimes called axes).

One vertical line and two receding lines at an angle of 30° are used to construct the drawing.

Therefore a simple cube would look like the drawing here.

Turn to page 66 for a quick guide to producing isometric drawings

Oblique drawing

Oblique drawing is simpler than isometric drawing; the front of the object is drawn parallel to the page, i.e. it looks flat to the viewer.

Features can therefore be drawn in normally, rather than at an angle of 30° –for example, circles can be drawn in as circles rather than as ellipses.

Turn to page 67 for a quick guide to producing oblique drawings

Assembly drawing

Assembly drawings are sometimes called general assembly drawings. This type of drawing is used to show a complete finished product with all the parts assembled in the correct position.

An assembly drawing may include overall dimensions with accompanying notes such as fitting instructions.

Assembly drawings are often produced using an orthographic view.

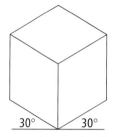

30° 30°

An isometric drawing of a cube

Isometric hole (shown as ellipse)

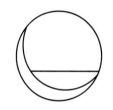

Oblique hole (shown as a circle)

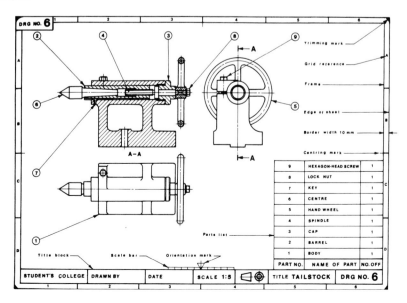

Adapted from Ostrowsky, O. (1989) *Engineering drawing: with CAD applications.* Edward Arnold

Exploded drawings

Exploded drawings are pictorial representations of all the component parts used within an assembly.

They are often used in manufacturing by the following personnel:

- sales and marketing staff use them to promote or sell a product
- maintenance teams use this type of drawing in equipment manuals when carrying out service and repair of machinery
- manufacturing personnel (who may not have been trained to read technical orthographic drawings) use exploded drawings to carry out assembly work on production lines.

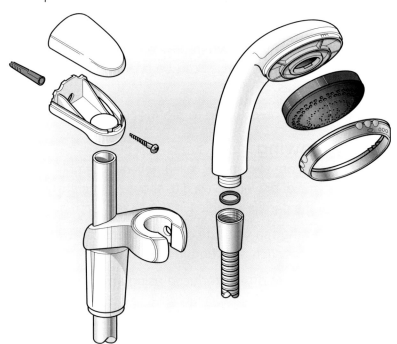

An exploded drawing of a shower head

Exploded diagrams can also be found in many handbooks for products you find around the home. They may include handbooks for:

- hand-held power tools
- flat-pack furniture kits
- model-making kits
- cars
- vacuum cleaners
- computer equipment and gaming consoles.

The use of CAD for design and 3D modelling

It is very common to use new technology to assist in the presentation of design solutions.

Computer aided design (CAD) is a type of software package used frequently by designers to illustrate realistically a finished design in the form of drawings, 3D models or animation.

CAD can also be used to calculate physical properties such as size, volume and weight, as well as performing scientific calculations such as force and stress analyses.

A further advantage is that CAD files can be transferred to prototyping machines which can produce complex components quickly.

Arguably the most aesthetic feature of CAD packages is the capacity to produce solid 3D models.

A model is a computerised image of the final product which shows what it will look like once it has been produced. A 3D model can be rotated so that all sides, edges and features can be examined in detail. With more advanced packages it is possible to animate the model.

Take a look at the example below. It is a model of our earlier mobile phone holder (see page 13), designed by a GCSE Manufacturing student.

The same technology that brings us animated films is used to design products like this mobile phone holder

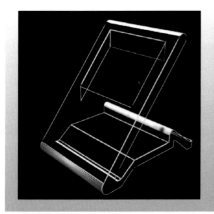

Modelling and prototyping

Models are used to illustrate what the product will look and feel like, how it will interact with other components, and with the environment for which it is intended.

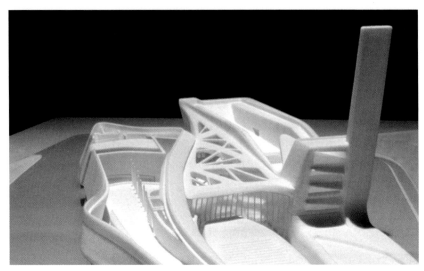

A digital photo of a model

Digital cameras can be used to produce images of the model to show the customer what the product will look like. As digital images can be easily modified, the product can be superimposed into different surroundings or environments by changing its colour and incorporating supporting notes.

The picture below shows how a product or person can be superimposed into a different situation.

These people have been digitally superimposed onto the image

THE
JARGON
DRAGON

prototype – a model of a product made before production to help designers

Upon the completion of technical drawings and possibly the generation of a computer model, the next stage is the creation of a physical model or prototype. This might be a representation in card, wood, plastic or metal.

A **prototype** is produced to demonstrate what the product will look like once finished. Prototypes are normally produced in very small quantities, often by a different technique from that used for the final product.

Prototypes are tools to determine whether there any faults in the design, or if there are any manufacturing problems. They can be used to test for properties such as strength, and to measure the life expectancy of a product. Before full production goes ahead, it is important that all these aspects are fully examined.

You may have seen prototype or concept cars demonstrated at motor shows on television. These cars look and feel like any other cars, but are produced only in very small numbers and by methods very different to those used for mass-produced cars.

Prototype vacuum cleaner

Prototype car

Rapid prototyping

Once a CAD file is produced on a software package it can be transferred to a rapid prototyping machine. These machines often look like coffee-vending machines and work in a variety of ways to produce a prototype product, usually from a polymer material such as ABS.

Some machines place layers of polymer, dispensed from a nozzle, building up to produce the finished component. Other machines use lasers to form parts.

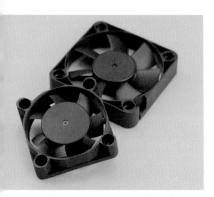

Prototype components (above)

Rapid prototyping machine (right)

The final design of a wind turbine (below)

An advantage of this type of equipment is that manufacturing companies can produce complex prototype components relatively inexpensively. Furthermore, the process is very quick; once the file is downloaded from the CAD system, the designer can set the machine away and concentrate on something else.

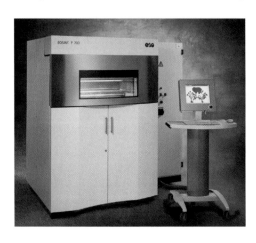

Prototype testing and evaluation

Reviewing a design constantly during its development is known as **value engineering**.

The more detailed the drawing the easier it is to produce a detailed evaluation.

As previously discussed, a prototype can be built before full production commences. This is an important time for evaluation as the product can be inspected, appraised and tested by many different groups of people.

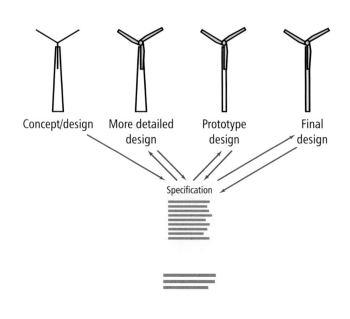

Concept/design   More detailed design   Prototype design   Final design

Specification

Justification of your final choice

Decisions, decisions! However many sketches, technical drawings, models, prototypes, tests, notes or modifications you have made, you must be able to make a final choice about exactly which product to produce.

The design specification is the main list of guidelines. So ask yourself – will your choice meet the agreed specification? You will need to evaluate how well the design relates to the original key features.

There are simply too many elements of the design to make a set formula for choosing the final design.

Example of a process of choosing a design

Key features		Product 1	Product 2	Product 3
Function	How well does the design work?	6	5	10
Quality standards	How well does it meet the quality standards?	4	5	10
Performance	What is the product's performance?	6	4	9
Intended markets	How well will it sell in the intended markets?	7	5	10
Size	How good is the size for the design?	9	5	2
Maintenance	How well can it be maintained?	10	5	1
Production methods	How accessible are the production methods?	10	6	10
Cost	What is the cost compared to competitors?	2	5	1
Regulations	Does it meet the regulations?	1	5	10
	Totals	55	45	63

Each key feature is marked out of ten

Excellent	7 to 10
Good	4 to 7
Poor	0 to 3

This is a numeric method of evaluating a product. It should be used with caution, for instance: we can see that product 2 scored the least, with 45 points, but it was not poor in any key feature consideration.

It is extremely important that every key feature is met. Product 1 is excellent in some areas, but is very poor at meeting regulations, so cannot realistically be considered at this stage.

You need to justify your final choice. If you can say that the product meets all requirements for the key features and the specification, your choice is justified. Clearly designers aim to achieve the highest possible rating in all the key features.

Even though the design specification is derived from the design brief, it is also worth comparing the final design with the original brief. Ask yourself if it satisfies the customer's original requirements.

There may be other factors not linked directly to the brief or the specification that have proved important in the development of the product. Take a look at the list of other factors.

Design requirements	Product 1	Product 2	Product 3
Physical and operational characteristics	5	4	10
Safety	5	5	10
Accuracy and reliability	6	4	9
Life of service	7	5	8
Shelf life	8	6	6
Operating environment	5	5	7
Ergonomics	4	4	10
Size	5	5	2
Weight	6	4	3
Materials	6	5	2
Aesthetics	2	4	7
Production characteristics			
Quantity	3	7	5
Target product cost	4	8	6
Miscellaneous			
Customer	7	4	6
Competition	8	4	7
Totals	81	74	98

Generally, decisions relating to the choice of final design will be customer-led but it is important for designers to present all the factors contributing to a safe, functional, worthwhile and quality product.

Testing the finished design

We are now in the final stages of designing a product – the testing.

Although designers can be very experienced at designing products, new products will need to be tested to ensure that they meet the specification and any relevant standards and regulations.

The product may contain new materials or include design features that have never been tested before. A series of functional tests will be needed to ensure that the product performs safely when it is being used for its intended purpose.

Testing is often time-consuming and expensive, so it is important to make sure that testing is carried out only on products for which the entire design process is complete, and that are fully developed and evaluated. If not, modifications and further developments may need to be made to the product, resulting in the testing process starting all over again.

Tests should aim to prove that the product can meet the key features of the design specification.

Function
The product should be made to perform its intended task. It is sometimes important to test a product until it breaks so that manufacturers know the limits of the product.

Quality standards
The product should be tested to make sure it complies with all relevant standards. These could be British Standards from The British Standards Institute (BSI) or European standards. The International Organisation for Standardisation (ISO) is a network of national standards institutes from over a hundred countries working in partnership with international organisations, governments, industries, businesses and consumer representatives.

The British Standards Institute (BSI) was founded in 1901. Its role is to set standards for products, to ensure that they are safe and practical.

Products that have been tested to British Standards will be able to carry the British Standard Kitemark logo.

Standard symbols exist to show consumers which standards the product has achieved.

The BSI kitemark logo

British Standards can apply to almost any product, for instance crash helmets, mountain bikes and skateboards. This system allows the customer to know that products are tested to a high quality.

Lives would be endangered if safety standards were not followed

Products that are sold in the European Union should be marked with the logo which shows that they have been manufactured to Central European Standards.

Britain operates in the European Union, so some British Standards (BS) and European standards have been harmonised. An example of this is:

BS EN 71 Manufacture of toys.

The directive sets out a list of requirements that toys must meet if they are to be sold in the European Union. If a product meets these standards, it is allowed to carry the CE mark. Note that this is not a safety mark, but one that allows the trade of the products in the European Union.

The CE mark indicates that these toys have been manufactured to the standards required by the European Union

BS EN 71 is broken down into six general areas of testing that need to take place:

1 mechanical and physical properties
2 flammability
3 migration of certain elements
4 experimental sets for chemical and other activities
5 chemical toy other than experimental sets
6 graphical symbol for age warning label.

Performance

The product will need to do the job that it was designed for. It may be tested for speed, strength, length of life, durability or any characteristic that it will require to fulfil its intended purpose.

Material properties can be tested in a number of ways; this information is used to predict how the product will perform.

Intended markets

Before products go into full production, it is useful to make an initial batch for potential customers to try out. Consumers can give feedback about the product which may criticise certain aspects. This constructive criticism can help designers make important modifications if necessary.

Size

The product will need to be tested for size, especially if it is intended to interact with a particular environment. Clothing, for example, must be tested to ensure compliance with standard sizes. The product may be part of a larger assembly, and be intended to fit into another product. When packaging is being developed, the size of the product needs to be taken into consideration.

Maintenance

When the product is completed it will undergo checks to see if it can be adequately maintained as intended. Sometimes screws cannot be fastened, oil may leak or dyes may run, making a product difficult, impossible or time-consuming to maintain.

Production methods

The production method needs to be considered well in advance of the testing stage to ensure it is compatible with the design.

However, the method can be practically evaluated during production.

It may be that a process is too slow or inaccurate to produce a component of the product. In this case an alternative method of production would be required.

Cost

The product's selling price will be estimated a long time before production begins, based on material, labour, equipment and overhead costs.

It is not unusual for development costs to rise during the design process, so the selling price needs to be checked against the actual processing costs. After all, manufacturing companies have one primary purpose – to make money!

Regulations

Regulations are rules that must be followed. These rules can be made in Europe originally and are known as EC directives. The government makes sure that the directives are met by developing regulations which businesses must follow.

An example regulation is The Management of Health and Safety at Work Regulations 1999 (SI 1999/3242) (EC Directive 89/391/EEC).

This safety regulation is commonly applied in businesses – you may see signs or certificates around workplaces to show that the company works to these regulations, ensuring a safe working environment.

The Health & Safety Executive (HSE) has produced approved codes of practice (ACoPs) which businesses can work to.

Scale of production

As with all new products, the quantity of products required to meet market demand is only an estimate. It is possible that demand for a product will grow, necessitating an increase in the scale of production.

Scales of production can be classed as:

- **small-scale** – small batches made largely by manual methods of processing
- **medium-scale** – medium batches produced in production cells, often using machine tools and automation

- **large-scale** – involving the use of production lines and highly automated equipment to produce large batches.

Modifying the design

When tests have been carried out, a lot of information is fed back to the designers. This allows the designers to make changes to the product's design. The design and subsequent drawings, models and prototypes are modified based upon the information taken from the tests.

If the product has a relatively long product life it is very common for other modifications to be made. In a competitive market many modifications are often fuelled by the desire for lower material or processing costs.

Other reasons why modifications might take place during production are:

- new regulations emerge relating to the product
- components change which mean design changes to the product must be made
- customer complaints
- safety issues
- new materials and processes are developed.

Modifications may improve the product but it is important to recognise the problems that might arise because of these changes – batches of the old design might have already been manufactured and held in stock. A decision must then be made either to continue supplying this product or to scrap it. Changes might also be required to products that interact with the product being changed – if you changed the plastic moulding of a TV remote control you would inevitably have to modify some of the components inside it.

When a product is being modified it is essential to update the corresponding drawings. These need to be marked with a new revision or issue number and date. The manufacturing personnel should then be instructed to dispose of the previous drawings and work only from the current issue.

Getting started on presenting your design solution

We have now introduced the fundamentals of designing a product; it is now worthwhile discussing how to present a chosen design. However, before we go any further, have a go at the activity below. The reason for doing so will become clear in a moment or two … .

Find a partner to assist you with this activity. It doesn't necessarily need to be fellow student – a friend or member of the family will also be able to help.

Find an object from around the house or classroom; preferably the object will include various features, shapes and dimensions – try not to pick something too simple or predictable.

1. Be careful not to tell your partner what the product is and don't allow them to see it.
2. Provide your partner with a pencil and a piece of paper and sit back-to-back with the object in front of you.
3. Try to describe the product's features to your partner so he or she can make a sketch of what you are describing – allow around 3–5 minutes to complete the sketch.

Have a look at a typical example below:

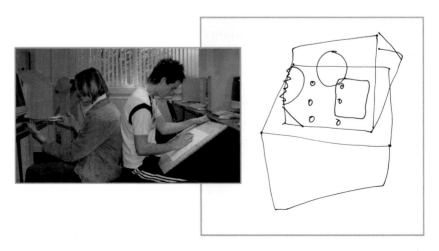

During an exercise like the one shown here, a student produced the sketch on the right from a verbal description

In general, students carrying out this exercise find the following common points:

- the drawing doesn't describe the product in sufficient detail
- the drawing isn't drawn to a scale nor does it contain any idea of size
- the object is usually drawn from one view only – often the easiest view that can be used to describe the product.

Unless the description is very clear the drawing partner will probably misinterpret several dimensions and features. In some cases they will even guess some of the features.

Students who achieve the best results tend to describe the product using very specific commands, such as 'Start with the bottom face – draw a line, approximately 10 cm long'.

The point of this activity is to demonstrate the most important reason for drawing to exact technical standards. This reason is **communication**.

THE JARGON DRAGON

communication – the verbal or non-verbal exchange of information

Communication

Remember that poor design is often the result of poor communication between the customer and the designer.

Communication is an important part of any activity and can be described as the passing on of information from one person to another. There are two types:

- verbal communication – talking to your friends and teachers, giving a presentation, giving instruction to a sports team-mate or working on a group activity
- non-verbal communication – writing an assignment, texting or e-mailing friends, drawing a picture, sign language or a physical gesture such as waving or smiling.

Good communication is vital in everyday life and it is also an essential element of manufacturing.

Once your design solution is complete you will need to communicate your ideas to a customer using both verbal and non-verbal techniques.

We'll start with the non-verbal technique known as drawing.

Using the phone, making a presentation, writing an e-mail and using sign language

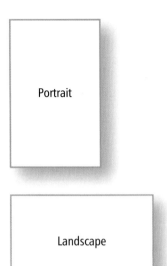

Portrait

Landscape

Paper orientation

Producing drawings

The first part of any drawing activity is to select the paper size and orientation.

If you have printed a document from a computer program such as Microsoft Word you may have noticed the option to print in landscape or portrait.

Within Word you also have the opportunity to select your preferred paper size. You will no doubt be aware that A4 is used as the standard paper size for printing most documents, such as your assignments, etc.

A3 paper is also popular and is commonly used for producing sketches – it is twice the size of A4.

The 'A' before the number indicates that the paper is a standard size; the number is used to represent the actual dimensions of the sheet.

'A' number	Size in mm
A4	210 × 297
A3	297 × 420
A2	420 × 594
A1	594 × 841
A0	841 × 1189

A0

A1

A2

A3

A4

Paper size

There are no rules stating what size of paper should be used for what purpose. A4, A3 and A2 tend to be most practical for our purposes.

Title blocks and borders

When producing a technical drawing it is essential to include a border and a title block (also good practice when sketching).

A border (or frame) is used to determine the limits of the drawing area, while the title block contains key information about the drawing, such as:

- the title of the drawing – this should include the design title
- the name of the person who has produced the drawing (sometimes initials suffice)
- the date the drawing was produced
- the drawing number and issue/revision number, ensuring the correct version is being used
- the scale of the drawing (the size of the drawing compared to the actual product; 1:1 would indicate a life-size drawing)
- the materials specified.

In many cases a grid referencing system can be used to assist in describing a particular feature on the drawing:

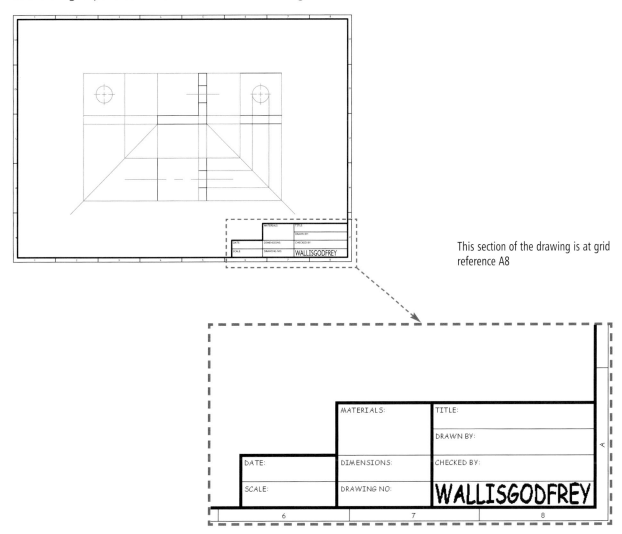

This section of the drawing is at grid reference A8

Drawing equipment

Producing sketches and technical drawings to a good standard requires very specific equipment to produce the best results. The most important tools are described below.

The pencil

Arguably the most important tool used in design, the pencil comes in various standard grades:

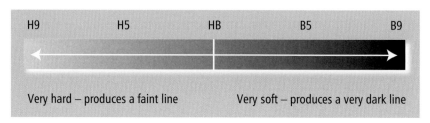

| H9 | H5 | HB | B5 | B9 |

Very hard – produces a faint line | Very soft – produces a very dark line

Pencil grades range from H9 to B9

Mechanical pencils are now widely used, and are supplied based on the diameter of graphite and the grade.

Coloured pencils are often used by designers when sketching or producing work for which colour is extremely important – in the textile industry, for example.

The eraser

Erasers are used by just about everyone to correct mistakes.

The rule

Again, the rule is a common tool used by students – usually to underline work.

In design, the rule is predominantly used to measure dimensions in both fractions of a metre (metric) and inches (imperial). The metric system is the standard choice of measurement in the UK.

The set square

The set square is commonly used by designers to produce straight lines and edges. When used in conjunction with a T-square it can produce lines at exactly 90°, 60°, 45° and 30° to each other. They can also be combined to produce multiple angles such as 75°.

The T-square

The T-square can be found mounted to a traditional drawing board using pulleys (called parallel motion squares) or used freely by running a straight edge along one side of the drawing board.

It is used to produce straight horizontal lines and provide a rest when using set squares. It is also normal practice for designers to line up their drawing paper using a T-square as a reference plane.

The fine liner

A fine liner pen is sometimes used to embolden or highlight certain features on an engineering drawing. Similar to a felt-tip pen, a fine liner produces a very clean, consistent line.

The compass

Another well-used tool in engineering drawing is the compass. It is easy, cheap and versatile method of producing circles of varying diameter and radius.

Dividers

Dividers are used to transfer distance from a measuring device to the paper, or in some cases from one drawing to another.

Similar in design to the compass, dividers have two points instead of one.

Templates and stencils

Templates and stencils come in various shapes and sizes and are used to produce standard symbols and text quickly.

Markers and highlighter pens

Markers and highlighter pens are useful tools to add colour or shading to a sketch. Generally try to use only one or two colours – a Technicolor mix of contrasting colours can lead to confusion, taking the emphasis away from the design solution.

Paints

Water, oil and acrylic based paints are often used in design at the concept stage, or by designers working in industries such as the textile industry, where colour and texture are of great importance.

We now know what drawing equipment is commonly used in design. We also know why borders and title blocks are used. The next stage is to produce a drawing. We have already covered the process of producing a sketch; it is now time to go one step further and produce some other types of drawing. A good place to start is with a simple perspective drawing.

Quick guide to perspective drawing

This type of drawing works by focusing on a vanishing point within the drawing that is used as a reference point. The vanishing point is the point where objects become out-of-sight.

The most common types of perspective drawing are one-point and two-point perspective.

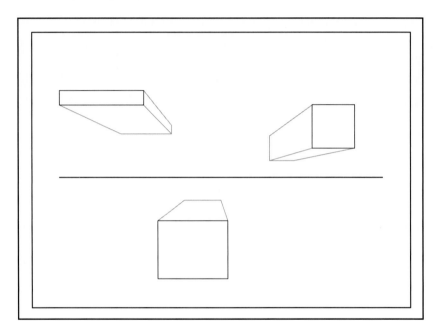

The diagram above shows a **one-point perspective** drawing of three simple cubes. Note that one face of each of the cubes is parallel to the picture frame, i.e. the nearest face looks rectangular to the viewer.

To sketch this out, follow the steps below:

1 Draw in a horizontal line to represent your horizon.
2 Pick a vanishing point on that line (the blue dot on the first diagram).
3 Draw a square anywhere on the page; note:
   a if you draw the square above the horizon, the cube will appear to be above the viewer
   b if you draw the square on the line it will appear to be at the same height (the exercise will not work if the square is drawn directly over the vanishing point)
   c if you draw the square below the line, the finished cube will appear to be below the viewer.
4 Draw a line from the corners of the square to the vanishing point.

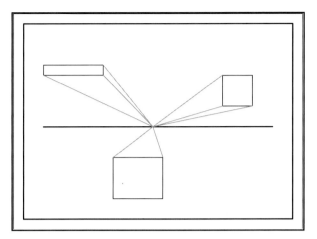

5 To finish, simply draw in the vertical and horizontal lines, to convey the depth of the object, and erase the construction lines.

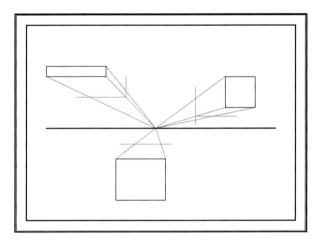

The drawing below shows a **two-point perspective** drawing of two cuboids.

This type of perspective is commonly used for engineering sketching; note that this drawing shows the cubes from an inclined view.

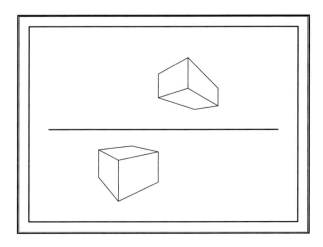

Many of the steps are very similar to those for one-point perspective drawing:

1 Draw in a horizontal line to represent your horizon.
2 Pick two distant vanishing points on this line.
3 Draw a vertical line of any height somewhere between these points – the height of this line will represent the height of your object at its nearest to the viewer.
4 Draw construction lines from each end of the vertical line to the two vanishing points.

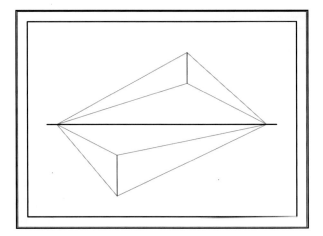

5 Draw in two further vertical lines on each side of the first vertical (keep between the construction lines). This is to convey the depth on each side and they don't necessarily need to be equal. If your object is on the horizon line then the object will be finished at this point.
6 If the object is above the horizon draw a construction line from the bottom of the two new vertical lines to the vanishing points. If the object is below the horizon draw a construction line from the top of the two new vertical lines to the vanishing points.

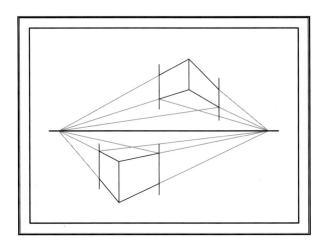

7 To finish, simply draw in the lines a little bolder to see the limits of your object.

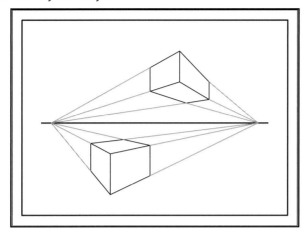

When drawing in perspective, if you are unsure where to draw the object with respect to the horizon, remember the following:

- small-scale objects look best just below the horizon
- human-scale objects look best on or just beneath the horizon
- large objects tend to lie in the middle of the horizon.

The drawing shown below is an example of a perspective drawing, and follows the same general rules (the artist has simply had a little more practice).

CENTRAL BOULEVARD

Quick guide to isometric drawings

Learning how to draw in isometric can be quite difficult at first (especially when producing circles and ellipses). The best way to learn is simply to have a go.

Using the following tools, redraw the isometric projection shown below – be careful to observe all the dimensions shown.

- pencil
- isometric paper or isometric grid included
- rule
- 30° set square
- drawing board and T-square (preferable).

Start with the bottom and outside edge, working inward to the top and inside faces. Leave the hole until last.

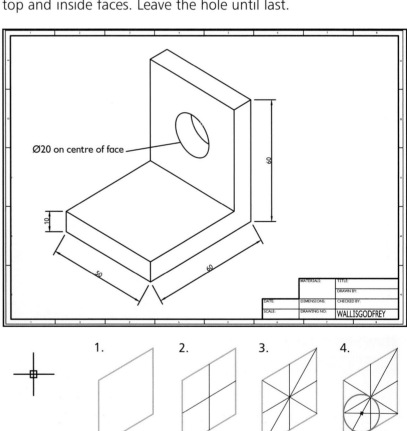

Ø20 on centre of face

WALLISGODFREY

Isometric projection

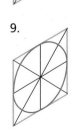

How to draw the circle

Quick guide to oblique drawings

The drawing below is an oblique projection. Using the following tools, have a go at producing the oblique drawing:

- pencil
- A3 or A4 paper
- rule
- 45° set square
- drawing board and T-square (preferable).

To complete the drawing, follow the stages below.

1   Start with the part of the drawing that appears parallel to you, i.e. the back face, which can be drawn in as a rectangle. The dimensions are 50 mm wide by 60 mm high.

2   At an angle of 45° draw in the length of the receding face – remember it should be drawn to half scale. The dimension is 60 mm so draw it in at 30 mm. The height can be drawn in the correct dimension, i.e. 10 mm.

3   Draw in the remaining features, including the circle.

4   Ask your teacher to check that the drawing is correct.

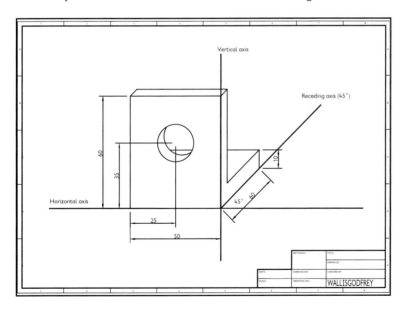

Oblique projection

Quick guide to orthographic drawings

As discussed previously, there are two methods of producing an orthographic drawing – as first-angle is more commonly used in the UK we'll look at this method in a little more detail. The process can become a little tricky at times so ask your teacher for help if you get stuck!

You will need:

- A3 paper
- pencil (2B and HB if possible)
- rule
- set square
- drawing board with T-square
- eraser.

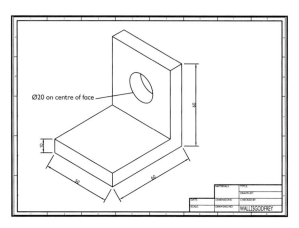

Orthographic projection

1 As usual, start with your border and title block.

2 Divide the paper up into three areas by drawing in two vertical construction lines (use a harder pencil so that these lines are faint and can be easily erased later on). These lines will represent the length of the object (in this case 60 mm).

3 Then draw in two horizontal construction lines: the first should be placed just above the centre of paper; the second will represent the height of the object (in this case, also 60 mm).

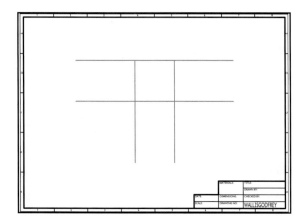

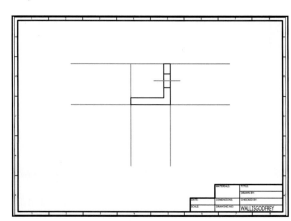

4 Using the correct equipment, draw in the front view using the dimensions shown – draw in the construction lines first, with faint lines, so that mistakes can be easily erased.

5 Once the front view is constructed to the required standard (check with your teacher if unsure), draw vertical lines down from all the key sides, edges and features.

6 Leaving a sensible space (see note below) draw in a box to represent the dimensions of the plan view – don't forget, this is looking down on the object.

To ensure the correct space between the plan and front view, generally you will need to remember:

- you may be required to draw in dimensions or notes
- if too bunched up, the drawing will become cluttered and possibly confusing to the viewer
- if neatly spaced out, the drawing will look much more presentable
- most importantly, the space between the front and plan views must measure exactly the same as the distance between the front and edge views
- if not considered correctly, all views might not fit on the same piece of drawing paper.

7 Draw in construction lines horizontally from the right of the front view to represent the key features.

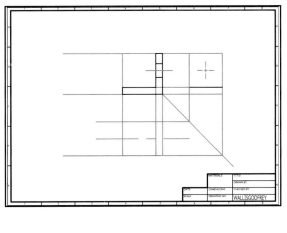

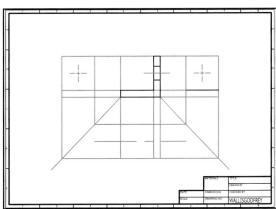

8 From the bottom right-hand corner of the front view, draw in a line of exactly 45° as shown (you will need to use the correct set square).

9 From the plan view draw construction lines to intersect the 45° line. At the intersection point draw a line vertically up – this will represent the features of the plan view as projected onto the side view.

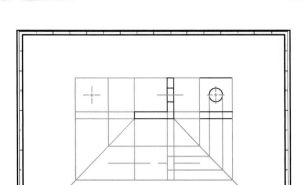
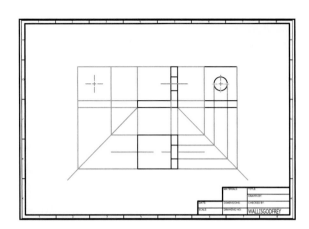

10 Once you have got this far, it is possible to add all the remaining features to the three new views by using a softer pencil to embolden all the key sides, edges and features.

11 Erase all construction lines.

Orthographic projection symbols

When producing drawings in first- or third-angle orthographic projection it is important to use a standard symbol to show which method is being used. This prevents confusion, as many manufacturing industries may use both techniques, especially international businesses.

First-angle projection symbol

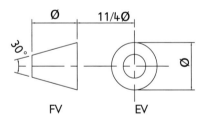

Third-angle projection symbol

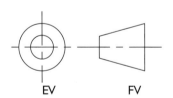

The symbols are shown above, with dimensional detail which describes how to draw each. The Ø denotes the diameter of the circle and can be drawn at any sensible size to fit into a title block.

Quick guide to the types of line used in technical drawing

One of the most important features of an technical drawing (particularly orthographic drawing) is the type and thickness of line used.

This is not dictated by the individual designer – the line type is set out in BS8888:2000.

The type and thickness of line are used to convey very specific information to the reader such as whether the line shows the outline or edge of an object, lines hidden from view and centre lines of holes, etc.

If the designer chooses not to use the standard types then the finished drawing could lack clarity, resulting in confusion.

The simplified version below shows the different types of line commonly used:

Line		Description	Application
A	————————	Continuous thick	Visible outline and edges
B	————————	Continuous thin	Dimension, projection and leader lines, hatching, outlines of revolved sections, short centre lines, imaginary intersections
C	∿∿	Continuous thin	Limits of partial or interrupted views and sections, if the limit is not an axis
D	—^—^—	Continuous thin straight with zig-zags	
E	– – – – – – –	Dashed thin	Hidden outlines and edges
F	—·—·—·—	Chain thin	Centre lines, lines of symmetry, trajectories and loci, pitch lines and pitch circles
G	⌐—·—·	Chain thin, thick at ends and changes of direction	Cutting planes
H	—··—··—··	Chain thin double dashed	Outlines and edges of adjacent parts, outlines and edges of alternative and extreme positions of movable parts, initial outlines prior to forming, bend lines on developed blanks or patterns

Quick guide to dimensioning drawings

Dimensions are vitally important when producing a technical drawing, to show the exact size of the features contained within the drawing.

Without adequate dimensioning, manufacturing of the product would become difficult, as the drawing would be unclear to engineers, leading to mistakes and assumptions.

Example of chain dimensioning

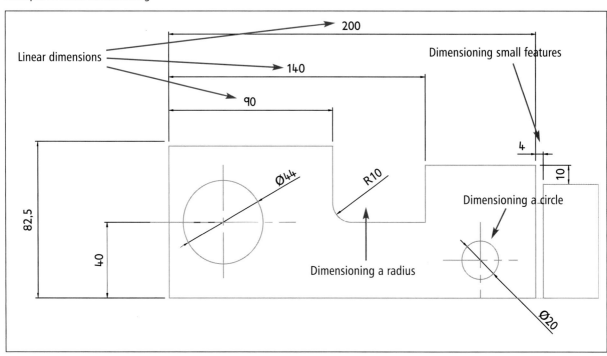

An example of a correctly constructed CAD drawing

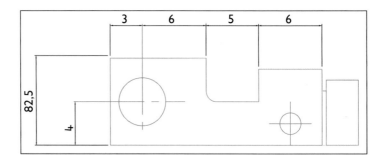

Dimensions should be clear, accurate, well spaced and follow the following guidelines, summarised from *A teacher's guide to BS8888*:

1 Each dimension required to define the object should need to be shown only once on the drawing.

2   There should be only those dimensions necessary to understand the object – extra dimensions with no value should not be included.

3   Linear (straight) dimensions should be expressed in millimetres; angular dimensions should be expressed in degrees.

4   Dimensions should be placed in the middle of a dimension line, either above it (if horizontal) or to the left (if vertical) – they should be placed so that they can be read from the bottom or the right-hand side of the page.

5   Dimensions should be placed off the drawing and should not be separated or crossed by other lines on the drawing.

6   Smaller dimensions should be positioned within larger dimensions – this is to ensure that the projection lines don't cross.

7   Projection lines should line up accurately with the feature they are dimensioning, leaving a small gap.

8   The projection line should extend slightly past the dimension line – usually 1 or 2 mm.

9   The arrows on the dimension line should be drawn neatly and uniformly. The point of the arrow should touch the projection line.

Completing your design portfolio

The completed design portfolio should contain the following elements:

- a design brief
- a design specification
- the generation of concept designs
- research notes
- an evaluation of the chosen design
- technical drawings
- a model or prototype
- notes on modifications
- a project diary containing an evaluation of the finished product and the processes involved.

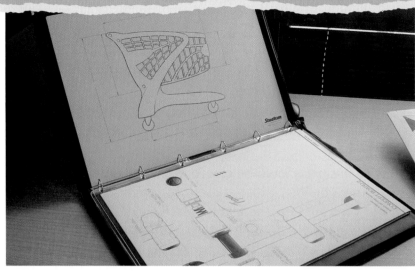

Design portfolio

The portfolio will contain all the work you have carried out in realising your design solution. You should include any notes, sketches, photographs, material samples, photocopies and printouts of relevant research, with explanations of how they have helped you in the design process.

Presenting your design to the customer

There is usually no need to show the customer the entire design portfolio. A summary of the main outcomes is often appropriate. Consequently there are several methods of presenting your design solution to the customer.

Display and mood boards

Display boards are very useful for showing sketches of the design with short relevant notes attached. Materials and fabrics can be added to the board, which is very appropriate in the fashion and textile industries.

Display board

Technical drawings

When a complex product with accurate dimensions is being produced, a technical drawing is very important. Used throughout the various sectors of manufacturing and engineering, a technical drawing is often of great importance.

Models or prototypes

It's always good to show the customer an example of the product. Models and prototypes are valuable in presenting your design solution to the customer, so that they can get an impression of the look and feel of the product.

Models are used throughout design and are one of the most important tools used by designers.

Oral presentation

Sometimes a formal presentation is called for. This involves the designer orally presenting the design solution to the customers. In this case the designer will often use one or more of the tools just mentioned. Designers (like many other professional people) may use ICT to assist them in the presentation. A common tool used for oral presentation is Microsoft PowerPoint, which you may have seen your teachers use in lessons. It is easy to use and provides an excellent method of visually displaying information. PowerPoint is very versatile and is a powerful tool when performing a presentation.

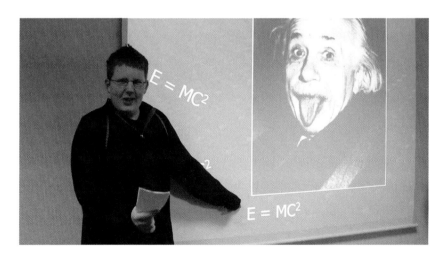

This student is practising his presentation with the aid of notes

Quick guide to producing a good PowerPoint presentation

1 Use a simple template or background – it's your work that you need to show off – a complex background can sometimes be distracting.

2 Don't have pages of text in a small font size – the audience will quickly become bored! Instead, use bullet points as subtitles and use a few notes (perhaps written on small cards) to expand on the key themes. Try not to read from PowerPoint or the cards; use them only as prompts. It's your design: be confident that you know it well and can explain the key features.

3 Use plenty of relevant pictures, sketches, diagrams, graphs, technical drawings and photographs – the better the illustrations, the better the presentation. If possible bring a model or prototype with you; otherwise, take a digital image or create a small movie clip – both can be placed into a PowerPoint presentation.

4 Don't stand in front of the projection equipment – you may find the presentation is being displayed on your forehead! Stand to the side so that the whole audience can see, and don't be afraid to look at the audience.

5 Don't forget to mention the brief and the specification: that's the reason you're doing the presentation in the first place!

6 Practise! There's a lot of truth in the old saying 'practice makes perfect'. Without practice you are essentially doing the presentation for the first time; with practice you could be doing it for the second, third or fourth time – it's obvious which will be the best.

Try not to stand between the projection equipment and the audience

Sports drink bottle

case study

This case study illustrates the design process in a simplified way, so that it is easy to follow. It contains all the key elements of the design process, while also referring to important aspects discussed previously in this unit. You can follow all the stages and maybe come up with your own design; even if you don't have the software needed to produce the computer-based drawings, you can still produce some sketches and diagrams. Alternatively, you can follow the stages involved in the design process, and hopefully improve your understanding.

The brief

A customer, needing a new product, has approached a design company. The customer is a major manufacturer of food and drink packaging and the product is a new bottle designed for sportspeople. The customer has issued the designer with the following design brief.

The consumption of water or sports drinks is an essential part of maintaining energy levels in sport. During a market research exercise, we discovered that athletes, swimmers and other sportspeople generally use drinks bottles similar to those used by cyclists; many of the people interviewed supported the idea of having a specifically designed sports bottle. At present, only a very small number of this type of product exists in the marketplace.

The key features of the intended product are as follows.

1. The container will hold at least 500 ml of fluid. Athletes/sportspeople must be able to carry it easily when running.
2. The bottle will retail toward the higher end of the present market, so the presentation of the container will need to provide the look and feel of excellent quality. In short, it should stand out from the crowd.
3. The material used will need to be easily cleaned and lend itself to mass production.

The labelling and branding design will follow that of the container; hence you have a blank canvas in terms of aesthetics (colour, style and form) and ergonomics (feel, size and shape).

case study

Sports drink bottle

The manager of the design company allocates the project to a designer named Richard.

Richard reads the brief carefully; he then decides to contact the customer's marketing department to ensure that he fully understands what they want from the design.

Once Richard is clear about what is required, he draws up his design specification.

Title	Sports drinks bottle
Function	Designed specifically for athletes and sportspeople to easily hold water or other consumable liquid
Quality standards	Designed to meet all relevant food and drink and processing standards
Styling aesthetics	Produced in a range of colours to a finishing standard. It must have a look and feel appropriate for the sports industry
Performance	Must store liquid safely, and be opened, closed and carried easily
Intended market	Athletes, sportspeople and sports teams
Size	Holds at least 500 ml of liquid
Ergonomics	Lightweight, no sharp edges, easy to carry and grip, incorporating an easy method of opening and closing
Maintenance	Easy to clean using water and mild detergent
Production methods	Lends itself to mass production with relatively low processing speeds and cost per unit.
Price	Recommended retail price of £12–£15 (towards the higher end of the current market)
Regulations	Complies with all relevant UK and European regulations
Scale of production	Mass produced at around 10 000 per run

Concept designing

Once happy with the brief, Richard decides to make a number of concept sketches of his vision for the product. These are shown opposite.

Richard presents his ideas to the customer. Both are well received, but they ask him to progress with idea 1.

Before Richard moves forward with his design he has some research to carry out: he must answer some important questions by consulting his colleagues, specialist manufacturing companies, text books and websites.

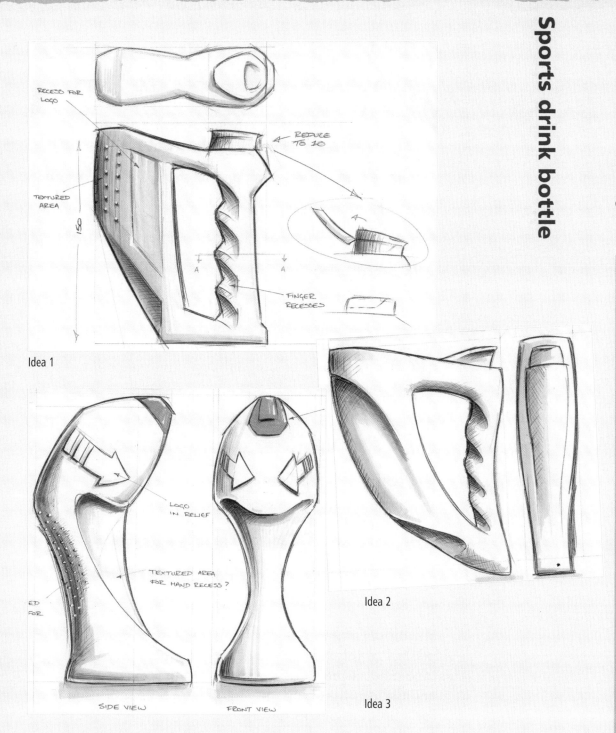

RECESS FOR
LOGO

REDUCE
TO 20

TEXTURED
AREA

150

A

A

FINGER
RECESSES

Idea 1

LOGO
IN RELIEF

TEXTURED AREA
FOR HAND RECESS ?

ED
FOR

Idea 2

SIDE VIEW   FRONT VIEW   Idea 3

What material should be used?

- The material must be easily shaped into the product with as little waste as possible.
- The material must be easily coloured, with a good surface smooth finish. The material must have the capacity to be cleaned using only water and mild detergent.

case study

Sports drink bottle

- The material must not react with the drinking liquid in such a way as to cause harm to the product user.
- The material must be stable and reliable, so the liquid is stored safely.
- The material must be sturdy, so that it retains its shape at all time, without being heavy.

Richard carries out research on materials, and decides that a thermoplastic polymer would be the most appropriate. These materials are easy to shape, lightweight, easily coloured, relatively cheap, and can be mass-produced.

Further research shows that food grade polypropylene (PP) or bottle grade polyethylene (PET) would be most suitable; both of these are recyclable materials. Richard decides that polypropylene would be the more appropriate choice, as it would provide a better feel of quality with denser colour, although the material would be slightly more expensive.

How should it be manufactured?

The manufacturing method must

- be able to accommodate large runs
- produce a suitable surface finish
- have a low cost per unit product (low cost for each bottle)
- not create a large amount of scrap product
- be able to process the chosen material.

The most common moulding methods associated with plastics of this type are injection moulding and blow moulding; Richard investigates both processing methods, and decides that blow moulding would be more suitable for a product of this nature.

What should the size and volume be?

To answer this question, Richard has to do a little calculation. He consults a science textbook to remind himself that 1 litre of fluid is equivalent to 1000 cm³ or 1 000 000 mm³. Therefore 500 millilitres (0.5 litres) must contain 500 000 mm³.

To ascertain the rough dimensions of the container, he needs to do the following calculation:

$\sqrt[3]{(500\ 000\ mm^3)} = 79.37$ mm (rounded up to 80 mm).

So if the container can measure 80 mm × 80 mm × 80 mm, it will have a volume of 512 000 mm³ , or 512 millilitres. Richard now knows that his product design must satisfy at least these minimum dimensions.

How should he present his final ideas?

He decides to present his findings to the customer using three main methods:

1　a 3D model on CAD
2　a prototype model made in ABS plastic
3　an orthographic technical drawing (following customer approval).

Richard produces a 3D model using CAD, based on his concept sketch. He uses CAD software to ensure that the dimensions will be suitable for the required volume of liquid, and to make minor adjustments to his design. His CAD drawing is shown below.

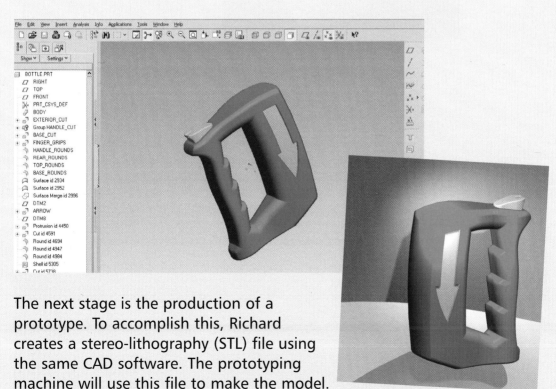

The next stage is the production of a prototype. To accomplish this, Richard creates a stereo-lithography (STL) file using the same CAD software. The prototyping machine will use this file to make the model.

case study

Sports drink bottle

The STL file is exported from CAD into the rapid prototyping machine, which builds up the product using layers of ABS thermoplastic polymer.

Below is an image of the finished prototype.

Richard demonstrates the prototype to the customer, who is delighted with the results, giving the go-ahead for Richard to produce the technical drawings shown below.

These drawings are sent to a specialist engineering tool-making company to design the mould tools that will be used to produce the actual product.

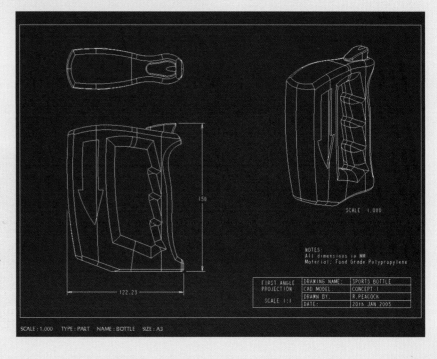

exercise

Design and graphical communication quiz

1 What is the difference between a design brief and a design specification?

2 Who generally supplies a design brief?

3 What are key features?

4 Why does a product need to be maintained?

5 Which of these is measured in kilogrammes?
- **a** mass
- **b** weight
- **c** density
- **d** volume

6 The unit of force is named after a famous British mathematician and physicist. What was his name?

7 Which of the following is NOT a method of joining used in manufacture?
- **a** adhesive
- **b** nails
- **c** forging
- **d** soldering

8 What is meant by the word Aesthetics?

9 What are the two methods of orthographic projection?

10 What does CAD stand for?

11 What is a prototype?

12 What does the following sign mean?

Answers on page 321

What's in this unit?

To complete this unit you will work as a member of a team to produce a batch of products. You will learn how to create and manage a team effectively.

As a team you will develop a production schedule from a production plan and will understand the importance of planning for manufacture and of recording information throughout the manufacturing process.

You will learn about the processes of a wide range of manufacturing systems from reviews of specific manufacturing sectors and case studies.

You will understand the role and importance of applying quality systems throughout a manufacturing process.

Manufactured Products

2

In this unit you will learn about:

Production plans and schedules for
manufacture   86

Resource requirements   97

The stages of production   101

Teamwork and team building   124

Preparation for manufacture   139

Manufacturing processes   141

Focus on paper and card production   165

Focus on the printing and publishing
industry   177

Focus on the textile industry   191

Focus on the pharmaceutical industry   206

Focus on the food manufacturing
industry   212

Health and safety   216

Applying quality and production
control techniques   221

Production plans and schedules for manufacture

Introduction

The majority of manufactured products contain more than one material, component or ingredient.

Have a look at any can of food – in this example we've used a popular type of canned product – baked beans.

Take a quick look at the label to see that the ingredients include beans, tomatoes (76% of the product), water, sugar, syrup, cornflour, salt, spirit vinegar, spice extracts and herb extracts.

It is unlikely that the manufacturing company will source these ingredients from one supplier – they will be purchased from different suppliers, probably in different parts of the world.

The can itself is made from recyclable steel or aluminium, and will be supplied from a specialist can manufacturing company. The label will be purchased from a printing company.

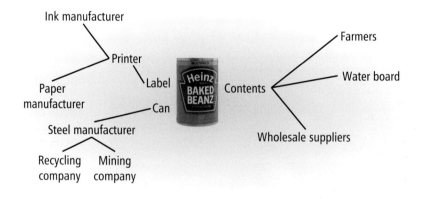

Resources contributing to a can of baked beans

All of these ingredients and materials must arrive on time to ensure that the company can produce the required quantity of canned beans each day – a shortage of even the smallest ingredient could prevent manufacturing taking place. The major manufacturers sell hundreds of thousands of this product every day; manufacturing at a reduced rate would lead to supplies soon running dry and would cost the industry millions of pounds.

The process of ensuring the materials, components and ingredients arrive on time is usually called material planning within manufacturing companies. Medium-sized and large organisations often employ staff dedicated to ensuring that buying and supplying of material happen on time and at the right price. These departments are normally called purchasing, **procurement** or the more informal term – buyers.

Once the materials, components and ingredients have all been purchased, the process of making the product in the correct sequence falls to a preparation technique termed production planning. This is the process of:

- ensuring that all the materials, components and ingredients are available at the right time
- making sure that tools, equipment and technology are ready to process the parts
- ensuring that the right amount of labour is available to guarantee efficient processing of the required amount of product
- ensuring that the **capacity** of the manufacturing process is not exceeded.

procurement – the acquisition of components, materials or services required for manufacturing, either from another part of the same company or from an external supplier

Modern methods of material and production planning

MRP II

Manufacturing resource planning (MRP II) is a method for the 'effective planning of all the resources of a manufacturing company' (Higgins, Leroy and Tierney, 1996).

capacity – the limit to the work that a company, workshop or area can undergo

It was developed from a system known as materials requirement planning (MRP), a method of using **bills of materials** (BOMs) and a master production schedule (MPS) to calculate all the materials and resources needed to produce products. The process can be very complex and may use databases to carry out the functions and calculations.

MRP II has three main features:

- the systems for a company's manufacturing and finance can be combined
- computer simulation can predict what is required for future manufacturing
- every part of a business is involved.

bill of material – list of all the materials and parts used to make the product – the cost and quantity of the components are generally always included

Just in time 'JIT' is a system used to ensure that materials arrive at the place where they need to be just in time. It aims to have no storing of raw materials or finished goods, saving time and money.

THE INSTITUTE OF
**OPERATIONS
MANAGEMENT**

The Institute of Operations
Management logo

A computer is made up of many tiny
components

JIT is a modification on the MRP II system. It is quite complex and manufacturing professionals need special training to use it.

The Institute of Operations Management is an organisation that trains specialists in this area. Try their website: http://iomnet. org.uk/index.htm.

New technology used in material and production planning

Just imagine how many parts are required to build a car, or how many components are used to make a computer. Both contain thousands and thousands of individual components, bought from different suppliers at different costs in different order quantities.

You will no doubt appreciate that getting them all together at the right time, ready for manufacturing, is not an easy task.

As this operation can be so detailed and complex, it is very common for new technology to assist with production planning. In many cases dedicated software is used to assist planners and engineers in what can be a highly complex buying and scheduling system. Automotive manufacturers have systems so advanced that you can find out the supplier name and address, batch number with supply date and cost of every individual component used to make any given car.

Smaller manufacturing companies or those with a smaller range of products or using fewer raw materials could possibly use one of the following popular software packages to assist with material and production planning.

Databases such as Microsoft Access

Databases are used to store and organise information for a number of different reasons, discussed in more detail within Unit 3: Application of Technology.

Businesses use Microsoft Access to store information about customers

Within the context of material and production planning, databases are used to store information on the following:

- information on products
  - part number
  - individual components used to make the product (BOM)
  - distribution of products (companies buying the product)
  - price of the product
  - details of products sold (cost/date/buyer)
- information on suppliers
  - name, address and other contact details
  - details of materials, components and ingredients supplied to the company
- information on components
  - individual part numbers
  - cost of individual parts
  - products on which the parts are used
  - required order quantities (the minimum amount of parts that can be purchased – this may be specified in units, weight or volume).

Spreadsheets such as Microsoft Excel

Spreadsheets can be used for storing much of the information previously described.

They can be also used to plan manufacturing operations in the manner shown below:

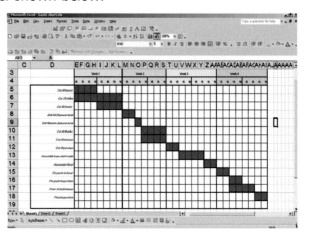

A Gantt Chart using Microsoft Excel

Spreadsheets are versatile software packages, described in more detail in Unit 3: Application of Technology.

Project planning software such as Microsoft Project

Project planning software has been devised primarily to assist with the organisation of tasks required to complete a manufacturing or management project. Examples of such projects could involve the building of a school, the prototyping of a new product or the implementation of a new software package into an organisation.

A package such as Microsoft Project is equally capable of assisting with the production planning of a product. The software can illustrate all the processing operations, the resources required and the time required to carry out each operation.

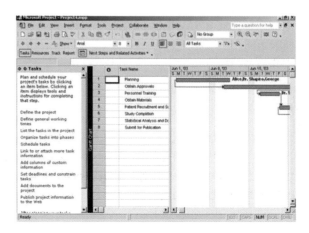

Microsoft Project enables everyone to see what should be happening at each stage

It can also be used to show all sub-operations (or **sub-assemblies**) and demonstrate how they are linked into the processing of the finished product.

Using this software it is possible to determine which processing operations are critical in ensuring the product is manufactured in the required time, i.e. those sub-assemblies for which a delay would result in the overall product being produced in an extended period of time.

Non-critical operations are those sub-assemblies that may be delayed without affecting the overall processing time.

THE JARGON DRAGON

sub-assembly – an assembled product that has to be assembled into a larger product

Production plans

A **production plan** is a document that provides all the information needed to produce a product. The information from a production plan is used to develop a **schedule for manufacture**.

Sample production plan

Customer		Product		Drawing number		Date required			Quantity	
Part number	Material type and size	Parts and components	Sequence of production	Process	Tools and equipment	Speeds and feeds	Health and safety	Quality control checks	Quality standards	Notes

A production plan contains a large amount of information.

Each section of information within the production plan is vitally important and ensures that products are manufactured correctly.

Let us consider more closely what is required in each section.

Part number

It is very important to be able to distinguish between the different products that a company produces. If a company produces only one or two products, they may be referred to by name. As the number of different products increases, it becomes more difficult to distinguish between them. Products are individually numbered or coded to make identification easier.

Each of the components within a product needs to be identified in turn so that when all the components come together the correct type is used.

Giving part numbers or codes to components

Here we see a box made up of eight parts:

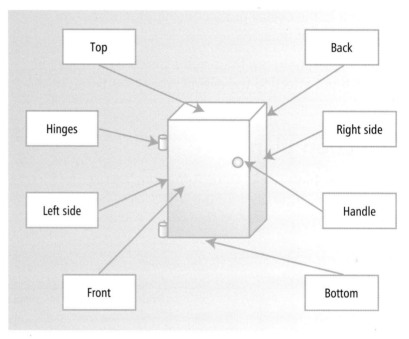

If we used the full name for each component, the documentation would be quite long-winded. It helps if we simplify parts using numbers or codes.

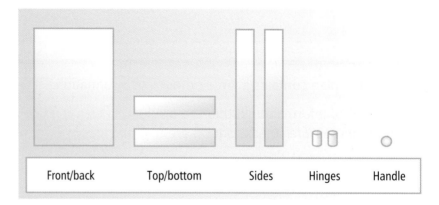

Looking closely at the components, we can see that the sides are exactly the same. We could call these 'Sides' or 'S'.

Similarly, the top and bottom are the same. We could call these 'Ends' or 'E'.

The back and door are the same at this early stage. We could call them 'B'.

When the front has the hinges and handle attached, it needs to be distinguishable from the back, so we could call this 'D'.

Hinges could be called 'H'.

The handle cannot have the code 'H' as it has already been used for the hinge – so we need to choose another letter – let's call it 'A'.

We now have a part number or code for each component!

Below we see the range of handles available to be assembled with the cupboard. Identify a coding system that will help you distinguish between each handle.

Consider all the variations, and consider how you would code any new products.

See page 321 for a solution.

ACTIVITY

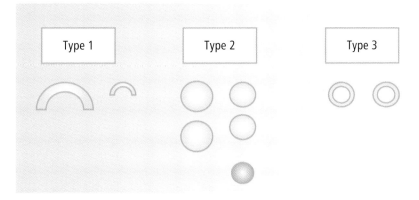

Type 1   Type 2   Type 3

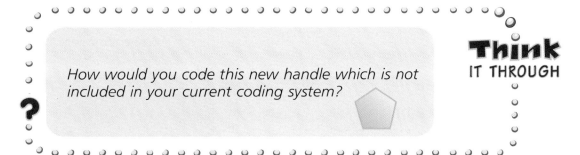

How would you code this new handle which is not included in your current coding system?

Think
IT THROUGH

?

Food

When coding food products, consideration must be given to variables such as flavour, colour, and types of food such as vegetarian or low-fat ingredients.

Clothing

Most people will be used to standard clothes and shoe sizes. Standard sizes needs to be applied throughout the manufacturing process to ensure a good quality product. Size will often be a key part of the product coding system.

Paper and card

There is a wide range of papers and cards varying in colour, size, density and weight as well as how the product is made and from which type of pulp. This will form the basis of the coding for this sector of manufacturing.

Material type and size

When specifying the type of material, component or ingredient to be used for a manufacturing process, it is important to identify clearly the key information regarding its supply. In other words, how will it arrive at the company?

The list to the left shows the main forms of supply.

Parts and components

All parts and components, however small, must be laid down on the production plan. This includes glues and fasteners.

Sequence of production

The order in which each component or part is manufactured and assembled needs to be very clear.

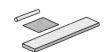
1. Collect material from stores

4. Drill holes

6. Assemble roof and fit perch

2. Mark and cut all panels

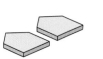
3. Mark and cut panels on front and back

5. Assemble sides to base

7. Inspect and paint

This should be described in a methodical way so that everyone understands what is going to happen and in what order.

Forms of supply

physical parts

length and thickness

weight

shape

type of material

properties

foods

liquids

solids

powders

containers (bottles, boxes, packets or sachets)

paper manufacture

reclaimed pulp

virgin pulp

paper and card processing

rolls

sheets

type

printing capability

food packaging

corrugated casing

clothing

fabrics rolls

yarn

textiles

cotton

nylon

PVC

wool

silk

Process

It is important to specify how the components are to be made. Instructions should be given to the manufacturing personnel so that each component is made in exactly the same way.

Sometimes, highly skilled workers need very little guidance other than a drawing or recipe, but in general it is good practice to be as clear as possible when describing how work should be carried out.

Diagrams, drawings and work instructions all help with this process. When giving instructions to people who will make the product, consideration must be given to the following:

- How skilled is the workforce?
- How well do you think workers will understand different types of instructions?
- What is the best way to get the information across – should an image, technical diagram or written instruction be included?

Tools and equipment

All the tools required to produce the product must be identified and listed. If the manufacturing process reaches a stage at which the tools or machines needed to continue are not available, then production will stop, causing great disruption.

Special tools and equipment

Often tools are standard, but there may be a need for special tools to be made especially for a particular product. Sometimes special holders are used to secure the work piece in place. These could be **jigs or fixtures**, sometimes needed to produce special moulds or patterns.

THE JARGON DRAGON

jigs and fixtures – special holding devices that make production easier

In some cases new machines and processing equipment such as ovens, sewing machines, image carriers or machine centres will need to be bought in order to produce new products. To have these facilities installed may be time-consuming and difficult to organise.

The life of tooling and equipment

All processes have an maximum rate, i.e. the maximum amount of work that a process can handle. If manufacturers push their processes past this rate then the processes could fail, resulting in the following:

- tools, blades or needles breaking under the strain

- products being burnt
- machines failing under the pressure
- poor quality in printing
- poor quality or dangerous products.

Processing time

Processing of any product will take time, which is often an important factor when pricing a product.

In most cases the tools and equipment used in manufacturing operate at varying speeds. Some scientific method of determining process time is typically used, often based upon previous times for similar work.

The speed at which components are produced is extremely important in determining the production time as accurately as possible so that the price can be calculated.

Health and safety

The production plan must contain information relating to health and safety, to ensure that the product is produced in a safe and responsible way.

This will include:

- personnel checks (qualifications)
- safety equipment needed (**PPE**)
- machine safety checks (maintenance records)
- material checks (**COSHH**)
- process checks (risk assessment).

PPE (personal protective equipment) – equipment such as boots, overalls and safety glasses used to protect people when working

COSHH (control of substances hazardous to health) – a special system for checking that hazardous materials are safely stored and used

Quality

Quality checks include a comparison of the product to a detailed specification. If processes are rushed, quality may become compromised.

So, working quickly is important to keep costs down, but working too fast can have disastrous consequences!

Think
IT THROUGH

Think of things you have done in everyday life where you have tried to go too fast, resulting in poor quality or complete failure!

?

Quality control checks

There must be a clear system of identifying how quality will be checked. This may include:

- measuring and calibrating tools
- technical drawings specifying key features
- checking against agreed samples
- detailing what, when and how to inspect
- procedures on how to check the product.

Resource requirements

Resources are all the things we need in order to make a product.

These resources can be categorised into different types:

- capital resources
- human resources
- material resources
- tooling resources
- service resources
- health and safety resources
- quality resources.

A resource planning sheet helps planners identify all the resources required for each stage of production.

Resource planning

Production stage	Capital resources	Human resources	Material resources	Tooling resources	Service resources	Health/safety resources	Quality resources
Preparation							
Processing							
Assembly							
Finishing							
Packaging							

This cyclonic de-stoner, designed to remove stones from potatoes at KP Foods, is a capital resource

Capital resources need to be replaced regularly or they will become liabilities rather than assets

Capital resources

These are the machines and processing equipment that will produce the components. Capital resources represent a large investment by the company. Industrial machinery and processing equipment will often cost hundreds of thousands of pounds and sometimes millions of pounds!

Capital resources reduce in value over time and eventually businesses will need to replace them.

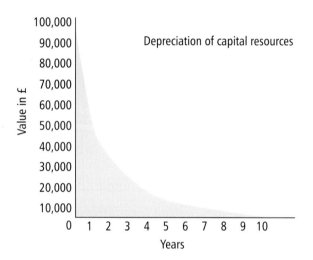

Human resources

Most business executives will admit that the most important resource required to manufacture their products are people – known as human resources in industry.

Manufacturing personnel include:

- managers
- engineers and technicians
- skilled trades-people
- quality control personnel
- process workers and operators
- trainees and apprentices.

Material resources

In order to produce products, materials are needed. These can be classified as:

- raw materials – the basic ingredients or materials bought in from the supplier, such as yarn in the textile industry, or ink in the printing industry
- bought-in parts – purchased as complete components such as nuts and bolts, or bottles and jars for food

- recycled material such as reclaimed pulp for the paper and card industry, or recycled polymers used to make drinks containers.

Suppliers of materials should be dependable for both quality and availability of products.

Tooling resources

In manufacturing, the term tooling is often confused with hand tools, such as spanners or screwdrivers – in fact it has a different meaning.

If we think of the capital resources as the main machine that can produce components, then the tooling is final part of the machine that does the work on the material. This could be the needle in a sewing machine, the image carrier in a printing system, or the blade that cuts food, paper or metal sheets.

Tooling undergoes a lot of work and will often need to be replaced owing to general wear and tear. Here are some typical examples of tooling from various sectors:

An injection moulding tool is a tooling resource

- food and drink — cutting blades
- paper and card — cutting and scoring blades, rollers with embossed patterns
- printing — image carriers, impression rollers
- textiles — shears, spinning rings, travellers
- clothing — needles, fabric cutting blades
- engineering fabrication — grinding wheels
- mechanical/automotive — spot welders and other end effectors for robots
- electrical/electronic — drills for printed circuit boards
- telecommunications — injection moulding tools.

Service resources

Service resources aid manufacture by supporting the process in one way or another. They do not add value to the product, although the company could not function without them. Service resources include maintenance, engineering, accounting, stock control, transport and purchasing.

Health and safety resources

Health and safety resources help to keep the manufacturing environment safe and healthy.

Specialist inspectors are a service resource

Typical health and safety signs

THE JARGON DRAGON

COSHH/PUWER – common regulations used in manufacturing. COSHH stands for Control of Substances Hazardous to Health and deals with the safe use and storage of chemicals and solvents such as paint and oil. PUWER, or Provision & Use of Work Equipment Regulations, deals with the safe use of equipment and machinery

Health and safety resources include:

- personal protective equipment (PPE) – gloves, safety goggles, ear defenders, boots and overalls
- safety regulations – health and safety regulations such as **COSHH** and **PUWER**
- personnel – first aiders, health and safety managers.

Quality resources

These are the resources required to ensure that products are made correctly and to the standards required. They could be:

- measuring equipment
- quality systems, e.g. ISO 9000
- personnel.

Measuring equipment

This is any device used to measure the product. This could range from complex measuring equipment needed to weigh ingredients for food, to simple devices that show whether a product is to standard.

THE JARGON DRAGON

ISO 9000 – a series of standards that specify the type of quality systems required to be implemented by a company

ISO (International Organisation for Standardisation) – an organisation with members in over a hundred countries, that sets standards for businesses. Visit their website at http://www.iso.org/

Quality systems

Quality systems are used to ensure that products meet the required standards. Sets of rules such as **ISO 9000** guide companies as to the best way to manage the quality of their products.

Quality personnel

These range from an inspector (who checks and tests the products) to the quality manager (who ensures that systems are in place to improve quality throughout the company).

The stages of production

The manufacture of products can be broken down into five basic production stages. These are:

- material preparation
- processing
- assembly
- finishing
- packaging.

When one stage is complete, the product moves onto the next stage.

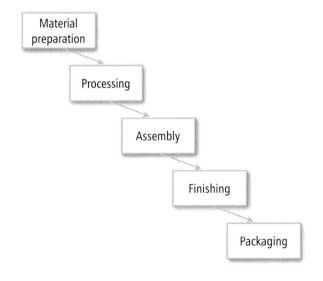

The main stages of production

What happens at each stage?

Material preparation

In order to make products, we need the basic materials. These are known as raw materials. It is usual that these raw materials need some type of preparation before they can be processed:

These preparation processes could be:

Sector	Typical preparation
food and drink	washing and peeling
paper and card	pulping and de-inking
printing	preparation of substrates
textiles	washing and bleaching

- clothing — checking colours and quality of fabrics
- engineering fabrication — checking material quality
- mechanical/automotive — ensuring stock is available
- electrical/electronic — ensuring chemicals and processes are correct
- telecommunications — ensuring cables are of correct specification.

Potato crisps coming out of the process of frying

Processing

This is when work takes place on the raw materials, changing their form in some way to add value. It is the main part of the manufacturing process but is not necessarily equivalent to completing the product. It could be baking, changing products chemically or changing the product by shaping, cutting, mixing or moulding the materials.

Assembly

Each individual part of a product is known as a component. These components are assembled or joined together by a variety of methods such as fastening, gluing and welding – this is the process known as assembly.

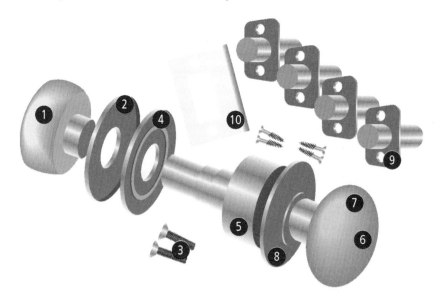

1. Inside knob
2. Inside rose
3. Mounting screws
4. Mounting plate
5. Cylindrical housing
6. Solid brass 6 pin cylinder
7. Removable exterior knob for quick rekeying or cylinder replacement
8. Outside rose adjust
9. 3-hour UL fire rated latch when specified
10. Strike

A sub-assembly of a door handle which will in turn be assembled in a door

In complicated products smaller assemblies known as sub-assemblies can be joined together to form a larger complete assembly.

Assembly could take place through the use of:

- adhesives and glues
- fasteners such as nuts, bolts, nails and screws
- welding.

Finishing

The manufacturing process that creates each component gives the component its main shape or form. A further operation is usually needed to give the component its final look. This process is known as finishing.

Finishing has a number of uses:

- to give the product a particular look or style
- to protect the product against the environment
- to make the product safe.

Packaging

Most products will need some type of packaging. Some products are strong and robust, whereas others are small and delicate, so the type of packaging will vary.

Packaging may be used to:

- protect the product from the environment
- protect the environment from the product
- give the product a particular look
- assist storage
- provide security.

There are many types of packaging, which could include:

- boxes
- cartons
- packets
- blister packs
- bottles
- drums
- cans
- vacuum-formed or injection-moulded plastic packages
- expanded polystyrene
- pressed cardboard.

Potato crisps are packed in foil and placed into corrugated cardboard boxes

Processing times

The manufacturing of any product takes some time, because each separate stage of production will take time:

- material preparation
- processing
- assembly
- finishing
- packaging.

The time for each operation is broken down into smaller parts:

- set-up time
- process time
- inspection time
- queuing time
- moving time.

Set-up time	Process time	Moving time	Queuing time	Inspection time
Total time to produce components				

Set-up time

The set-up refers to the process of ensuring that the material is fixed in the correct position and the processing stage is ready to start.

Before any component or part can be made, the raw material needs to be placed in a machine or a manufacturing station. The work-holding device may need to be set or prepared to take the raw materials.

Tools may need to be sharpened, prepared or fitted in position. The set-up itself may need to be overseen by a supervisor. All of these elements of the set-up take time and should be considered during planning.

Processing time

The processing time is the time taken to produce the component. This could be a manual process, whereby a skilled worker produces the component by hand, a machining process whereby a skilled worker uses a machine to produce the work, or a fully automatic process whereby a machine completely produces the component at the touch of a button.

Processing time for manual production is more difficult to estimate as it is extremely variable. Fully automated systems will produce each part in exactly the same time.

Moving time

Each time a product is moved it takes time. Moving time could include moving a product by hand from one work bench to another or to different areas of the process by conveyor, trolley or an automated guided vehicle. The product could also be moved to different businesses around the world by rail, air or sea. It is important to consider this movement, as it can dramatically influence the time it takes to produce a product.

Potatoes move around a potato crisp factory on conveyors

Queuing time

When components are manufactured, each process takes time. If a product is processed in a short time at one stage and arrives early at the next process which takes longer, a queue will form. This creates a number of problems in production; planners must take into account the time that queuing adds to production.

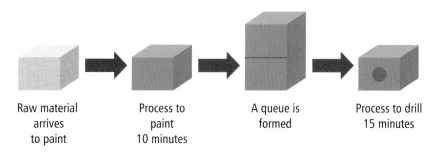

| Raw material arrives to paint | Process to paint 10 minutes | A queue is formed | Process to drill 15 minutes |

Queuing problems may occur when processes need to take place sequentially

Inspection time

The amount of time spent checking and inspecting products can vary enormously. This time needs to be taken into account when planning.

Low quality products may be checked infrequently but high quality products may need thorough inspection before being sent to the next stage of production, or to the customer.

In teams of five you will produce a batch of five small card holders.

You will require:

- several sheets of A4 paper
- scissors
- stapler and staples
- rule
- a watch with a second hand.

The three operations are as follows.

1 Take a sheet of A4 paper, fold it in half lengthways, and cut it with scissors.

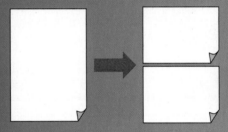

2 Fold the top edge over 10–15 mm.

3 Fold in half and staple in three places as shown, 10–15 mm from the edges.

← Open end

4 Inspect the product.

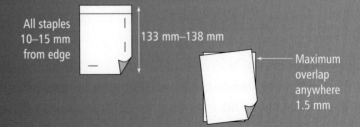

All staples 10–15 mm from edge

133 mm–138 mm

Maximum overlap anywhere 1.5 mm

Envelopes must meet all the inspection criteria.

Task

Sit around a table or desk that is big enough to produce a batch of five envelopes. You will produce a single envelope and then a batch of five.

Decide how the cell will be laid out to produce the envelopes.

Practise each operation and use a watch to determine a time for each operation.

Here are some example times (but you should use your own times):

Operations	Time, seconds
1 Fold and cut A4 sheet	12
2 Fold edge 10 mm–15 mm	8
3 Fold envelope and staple	10
4 Inspection	12

As a team, discuss any queuing problems that you think might occur. Discuss the times taken to move materials around the desk.

Producing a single envelope

Copy and complete the following table to determine the total time.

Operations	
1 Fold and cut A4 sheet	seconds
2 Fold edge 10 mm–15 mm	seconds
3 Fold envelope and staple	seconds
4 Inspection	seconds
Additional times	
Queuing	seconds
Material movement	seconds (total)
Total time	seconds

Example table
(times on this table should be used only as a guide).

Operations	
1 Fold and cut A4 sheet	12 seconds
2 Fold edge 10 mm–15 mm	8 seconds
3 Fold envelope and staple	10 seconds
4 Inspection	12 seconds
Additional times	
Queuing	0 seconds*
Material movement	6 seconds (total)
Total time	48 seconds

* No queuing with one product

A schedule of envelope production

A Gantt chart shows the production schedule of a single envelope.

We have estimated set-up time as 10 seconds. This includes laying out the table ready for production.

The Gantt chart shows the timing for each operation. Each operator has a number.

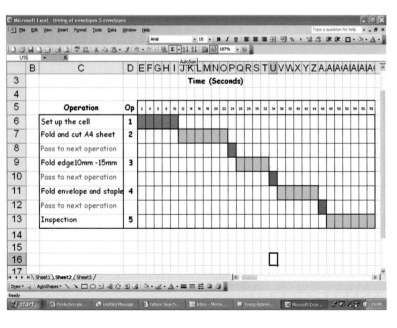

Operator 1 will set everything up in the first 10 seconds.

Operator 2 will fold and cut the A4 sheet from between 10 seconds to 22 seconds, then pass it to Operator 3.

The process will continue until the product is complete in 48 seconds, plus 10 seconds for set-up: 58 seconds in total.

Now produce a single envelope. Use a watch to time the process and compare the actual time with the planned time.

Producing a batch of five envelopes

We can see how producing a batch makes a difference to the Gantt chart. The first envelope is shown with blue blocks. The second envelope is shown with orange blocks, and so on.

It can be seen that Operator 2 can continue on to the next envelope immediately but Operator 3 has to wait each time for the cutting and folding to take place. This is known as idle time: the operator is not doing work. This is costly because he continues to be paid by the company.

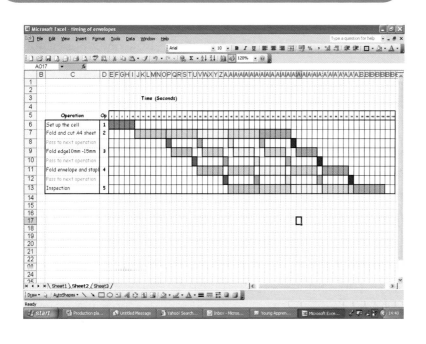

Availability of stock

At each stage of production, material should be available to make the product. Let's take the example of a G-clamp.

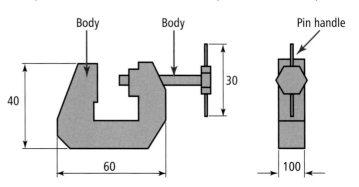

Example drawing of a G-clamp

Calculating material usage

A simple G-clamp is manufactured with three components:

- body
- screw
- pin handle.

100 G-clamps are to be made per hour, cut from a bar that measures 40 mm wide × 10 mm thick × 2000 mm (2 m) long.

The body measures 60 mm × 40 mm × 10 mm in plain carbon steel.

The screws are bought in boxes of 20 and have a 3 mm hole drilled in the head.

The pin is 30 mm long, cut from a 3 mm diameter × 3 m long bar

To ensure that there is enough material available, we will need to make available the following amount of material per hour.

Material ordering

1 The body: 60 mm × 40 mm.
   100 components × 60 mm long = 6000 mm or 6 m
                                                      = 3 bars per hour.

2 The screws:
   100 components ÷ 20 screws per box $= \dfrac{100}{20}$

                                                    = 5 boxes per hour.

3 Pin handles: 30 mm long.
   100 components × 30 mm = 3000 mm or 3 m
                                      = 1 bar per hour.

If the screws are not ready, then the pins cannot be assembled. If the pins are not ready then the G-clamp cannot be finished. You need to recognise the importance of making sure materials and components are available at the right time.

Applying planning and scheduling techniques

In order to understand more fully the planning and preparation required to produce a batch of products, look at the case study starting on the next page. It highlights the process of scheduling and control, essential for an effective manufacturing team.

case study

Bird house manufacture

A team of 15 students is to produce a batch of 10 bird houses as shown. They are given the drawing (below), a product specification and a production plan. They will decide who should undertake which role, and will organise and manage the whole process, with some supervision from the teacher.

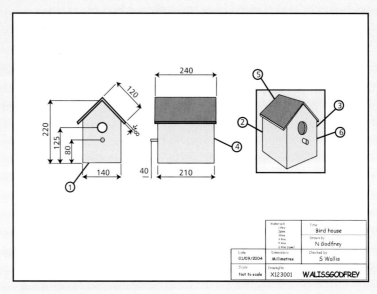

Drawing given to the students

Product Specification

Bird house Drawing Number X123001

Materials
- Sides: Pine
- Front: Pine
- Back: Pine
- Base: Pine
- Roof: Pine
- Perch: 10mm pine dowel 10mm
- Wood nails: Mild steel
- Glue

Measurement all dimensions in mm ±2 mm

Critical control points
- Check front, back and base for size.
- Check hole diameter and position.
- Check assembly before roof is added.

Finish
- Two coatings of water based wood preserver (Pine). See sample.
- Roof two coatings of water based wood preserver (Dark oak). See sample.
- Smooth to touch with no sharp corners or splinters.

Quality indicators
- Smooth surfaces
- All wood is coated
- Perch is solid

Product specification given to the students

Production plan given to the students

Customer Garden Leaf Ltd		Product Bird house		Drawing number X123001			Date required Oct-05		Quantity 10	
Part No.	Material type and size	Parts and components	Sequence of production	Process	Tools and equipment	Speeds and feeds	Health and safety	Quality control checks	Quality standards	Notes
1	Pine 140 × 210 × 11	Base	Cut to size Sandpaper edges Check	Hand tools	Saw/ file		Supervision	Ruler to check sizes	Made to drawing	Watch for splinters
2	Pine 150 × 210 × 11	Sides	Cut to size Sandpaper edges Check	Hand tools	Saw/ file		Supervision	Ruler to check sizes	Made to drawing	
3	Pine 140 × 220 × 11	Front	Cut to size Sandpaper edges Drill 40 diameter hole Drill 10 diameter hole Check	Hand tools	Saw/ file/ Drill	500 rev/min	Goggles Supervision Supervision	Ruler to check angles Sizes	Made to drawing Hole accepts gauge	Be careful when drilling Sandpaper entrance hole
4	Pine 140 × 220 × 11	Back	Cut and drill Sandpaper edges Check	Hand tools	Saw/ file		Supervision	Ruler to check sizes	Made to drawing	
5	Chipboard 120 × 230 × 9	Roof	Cut to size File angle at joint Check	Drilling	Saw/ file/ hammer		Supervision	Ruler to check sizes	Made to drawing	Make sure the joint is neat
6	Dowel 10 mm diameter	Perch Sandpaper edges Glue and fit into hole Assemble Paint Inspect	Cut to length	Assembly	Saw/ file Hammer Water based paint Rule Colour samples		Be careful with glue	Ruler to check sizes	Fit into hole	Make sure there is glue on dowel before assembly

Deciding who will do which job

The team sits down to discuss who will fulfil which role.
They are given a blank **organisation chart** which
identifies the roles available.

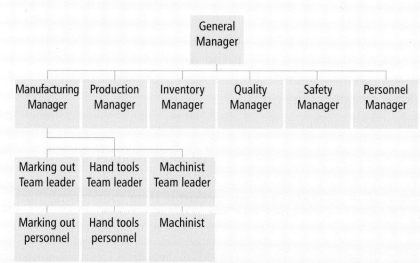

THE JARGON DRAGON

organisation chart – a diagram which shows all the members of a team or business. It aids communication by showing who is managing whom, and who is responsible for each role

case study

Bird house manufacture

In a meeting, the students will decide who will undertake each role. They are given a short description of each of the roles to help them decide.

Description of roles

General manager
This person has overall responsibility for producing the work to the correct quality in the correct time. They have to balance the needs of all the managers.

Manufacturing manager
This person controls all the tasks associated with making the components. The production manager agrees with the manufacturing manager what should be made in the session. The manufacturing manager then gives instructions to their personnel on what they need to be working on.

Production manager
This person is responsible for planning and preparation, i.e. what needs to be done on each session – this must be agreed with the manufacturing manager. The production manager needs to be very well organised, with good leadership skills.

Inventory manager
This person ensures that all materials and components are accounted for and do not go missing. They should know whether material is being worked upon (work in progress) or if it is finished.

Quality manager
The quality manager makes sure that everything is made to the standards set out in the product specification. They often have to slow down or even stop production in order to get things right.

Safety manager
The safety manager ensures that all personnel are working safely. They might supervise fire drills or produce posters. They can stop production if they think something is unsafe.

Personnel manager

The personnel manager ensures that there are enough people with the right skills to complete the work. They might also deal with complaints from personnel, or need to speak to personnel about inappropriate behaviour.

Marking out personnel

These team members mark out the products to be cut. They need good measurement and drawing skills, and patience.

Hand tool personnel

Hand tool personnel make the products using hand tools. They cut, join and finish the components. They must have good hand skills and be fast and accurate workers.

Machinists

These team members use the machines to drill, cut or join the components. They must be responsible, mature and safety-conscious. It is important that work with moving machinery is supervised by a suitably qualified person.

Deciding who does which role

After a long discussion the team produces the minutes of the meeting which say who will do each job and why.

Minutes of team meeting

September 19, 2004

Present:

Matthew (chairperson)	Helga	Rebecca
James	Anne-Marie	William
Ryan	Hannah	Sam
Evan	Chloe	Stephanie
Olavia	Vici	Nicola

General manager

Matthew is good at organising and is a good communicator. He plays rugby for his school and knows that when his team is struggling he can fire them up.

Manufacturing manager

James has good knowledge of how to produce things. He loves working with his hands, is energetic and can talk to people easily. James is popular and will do jobs for people without complaint.

Machinists

Ryan loves gadgets and mechanisms and is always thinking up ways to improve things. He is mature, trustworthy, and will make an excellent machinist team leader.

Evan is trustworthy and has good concentration skills.

Hand tools personnel

Olavia likes to roll up her sleeves and do some work. She always takes pride in her work and will make a first-class team leader.

Rebecca's work in the workshop is usually the best in the class and is always accurate.

William likes anything to do with technology and making things. He is a hard worker.

Marking out personnel

Sam is a bit of an artist who loves drawing and has an eye for detail – he will be the team leader.

Helga is patient and has great concentration. She won't rush anything but prefers to have things exactly right.

Production manager

Hannah is good at communication and great at mental arithmetic. She loves making things and has strong leadership skills. She likes to keep an eye on the players in her football team and give them instructions when needed.

Anne-Marie is interested in art and design. She is excellent at drawing and can work accurately.

Inventory manager

Chloe is a good organiser and always likes to know where everything is. She was in her maths master class so is good with numbers.

Quality manager

Vici is fussy about things being just right and will not accept second best – she will make a very good quality manager.

Safety manager

Stephanie is a good communicator with loads of common sense. Her dad is in the army; she knows the importance of teamwork and discipline. She can see dangerous things around the workshop and is quite mature for her age.

Personnel manager

Nicola is great with everyone and can get the best out of people. She can tell if someone is feeling upset and is always able to cheer them up.

The minutes of the meeting are distributed to all team members

A completed chart is produced by the personnel manager (Nicola).

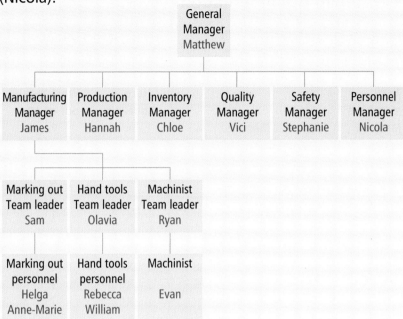

Production documentation

Each manager in the team completes documentation given to them which will record decisions and issues. Here we see all the managers' reports for the first week (the blue writing indicates where the students have written).

Quality control

Quality manager: Rebecca   Week number 1

Quality standards met

	Measurements	Finish	Assembly
Base	ok	ok	
Sides	Wood is cracked		
Front	ok	ok	
Back	ok		
Roof	Too small		
Perch	Too short		

Quality issues   Date: 15 October

1 Perches are being cut too short.
2 Two components are being stacked up in a dirty bench.
3 Wood is cracking in vice.

Actions   Date: 15 October

1 Train perch cutters how to cut to length.
2 Find clean dry place to store cut wood.
3 Train wood sawyers how to hold wood.

case study

Bird house manufacture

Personnel documentation

Personnel Manager: Nicola   Date: 15 October

Week number 1

Team members		Here X, Absent A	Work rate out of 10
Matthew	General Manager	X	7
James	Manufacturing Manager	X	5
Ryan	Machinist Team leader	A	–
Evan	Machinist	X	8
Olavia	Hand tools Team leader	X	9
Rebecca	Hand tool personnel	X	7
William	Hand tools personnel	X	7
Sam	Marking out Team leader	A	–
Helga	Marking out personnel	X	10
Anne-Marie	Marking out personnel	X	9
Hannah	Production Manager	X	7
Chloe	Inventory Manager	X	6
Vici	Quality Manager	X	9
Stephanie	Safety Manager	X	5
Nicola	Personnel Manager	X	7

Personnel issues   Date: 15 October

1 Sam is ill and will be absent for 2 weeks.
2 Ryan doesn't like being a machinist so he will swap with Rebecca.
3 Helga is working really hard. This should be recognised.

Actions   Date: 15 October

1 Hannah will help out in marking out to cover for Sam.
2 Swap Ryan with Rebecca.
3 Give Helga certificate at end of lesson.

The team recognises
the hard work and dedication
of
Helga

Personnel Manager
Nicola
General Manager
Matthew

Safety documentation

Safety Manager: Stephanie   **Date** 15 October
Week number 1

Safety rules

1) Always wear boots and overalls.
2) Wear goggles when drilling.
3) No running or messing about in the workshop.
4) Always get supervision when drilling.
5) Report any accidents to the teacher.

Safety issues

Date 15 October

1) People are leaving shoes and bags on the workshop floor.
2) There are some boxes stacked up in the corner which could be dangerous.
3) People keep getting splinters when carrying the cut wood.

Accidents

4) Vici cut her finger on a saw. The teacher was told and the first aider came.
5) Olavia walked into the side of the table and bruised her leg.

Actions for next week

1) Make sure personnel are told to wear gloves when carrying wood from stores.
2) Make poster about being careful around benches.
3) Practise fire drill.

Always use gloves

when lifting wood from the stores!

case study

Bird house manufacture

Stock control documentation
Inventory manager: Chloe　　　　　　Date 15 October

Week number 1

Material required

Base	1	× 10 =	10
Sides	2	× 10 =	20
Front	1	× 10 =	10
Back	1	× 10 =	10
Roof	2	× 10 =	20
Perch	1	× 10 =	10
Nails	24	× 10 =	240
Glue	5 ml	× 10 =	50 ml
Paint	(Oak)		0.5 litres
Paint	(Teak)		0.5 litres

Date 15 October

Start of production

	Base	Sides	Front	Base	Roof	Perch	Nails
Raw material	10	20	10	10	20	10	240
Work in progress	0	0	0	0	0	0	0
Finished goods	0	0	0	0	0	0	0

End of production

	Base	Sides	Front	Base	Roof	Perch	Nails
Raw material	0	0	0	10	20	10	240
Work in progress	0	0	10	0	0	0	0
Finished goods	10	20	0	0	0	0	0

case study

The production manager produces a schedule in the form of a Gantt chart. This will be the overall plan for production.

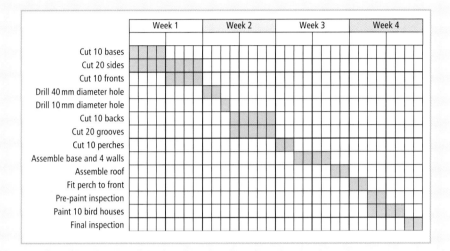

	Week 1	Week 2	Week 3	Week 4
Cut 10 bases				
Cut 20 sides				
Cut 10 fronts				
Drill 40 mm diameter hole				
Drill 10 mm diameter hole				
Cut 10 backs				
Cut 20 grooves				
Cut 10 perches				
Assemble base and 4 walls				
Assemble roof				
Fit perch to front				
Pre-paint inspection				
Paint 10 bird houses				
Final inspection				

The production manager produces a diagram showing how the product will be produced.

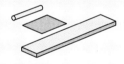

1. Collect material from stores

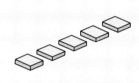

2. Mark and cut all panels

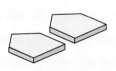

3. Mark and cut panels on front and back

4. Drill holes

5. Assemble sides to base

6. Assemble roof and fit perch

7. Inspect and paint

case study

Bird house manufacture

Production manager documentation

Inventory manager: Hannah   Date 15 October

Week number 1

Material required	Quantity planned	Quantity actual
Base		
Mark out	10	10
Cut	10	10
Sand paper	10	10
Sides		
Mark out	10	10
Cut	10	10
Sand paper	10	10
Front		
Mark out	10	10
Cut	10	5
Sand paper	10	2
Back		
Mark out		
Cut		
Sand paper		
Roof		
Mark out		
Cut		
Sand paper		
Perch		
Mark out		
Cut		
Sand paper		

Production Report

It was difficult to organise marking out. Sam was absent so it was difficult to get things done. Olavia hurt her leg and stopped work for a sit down. All this meant that we couldn't complete the work that we had to do. Next week Nicola will help out cutting the components so we can catch up on production

---

General manager documentation

Inventory manager: Matthew   Date 15 October

Week number 1

Management Report

1) The team is working well together with only a few small issues such as swapping roles
2) Safety is good but there will be a safety poster produced on lifting wood for next week.
3) The level of quality is ok but will improve next week .

Production is behind but plans have been made for next week to catch up.

The team continues the process, following the production schedule, until the order is complete.

The finished products

Teamwork and team building

team – a group of two or more people working together towards a common goal

Whenever someone is given any type of task they always have to answer the following question: am I going to do the work alone, with a partner or in a **team**?

In manufacturing there are generally many people involved. In order for the business to be successful people must work together in teams.

Teamwork is essential if a group of people working together is to be successful in meeting its objectives.

These pumpkin handlers have broken down their task to increase efficiency

Allocating and agreeing roles and responsibilities

The work that needs to be carried out can be broken down into smaller tasks so that each of the team members can be allocated simpler tasks.

Allocating tasks

There are several ways in which the tasks can be allocated:

- a team leader or chairman can allocate each task to a team member
- team members can request that they do particular tasks
- the team can sit down together, discuss problems as a group, and find solutions.

Think IT THROUGH

Consider some different types of teams.

Who decides who does what in the following teams:

- *football team*
- *the army*
- *manufacturing production team?*

People often function more effectively when they work in areas in which they already have relevant skills or ability.

Consider the following list. Think about how good you are at a particular aspect and discuss your results in small groups.

What are your strengths?

Are you good at maths?

Are you good at communications and working with other people?

Are you good at IT?

Do you like doing presentations?

Do you like to manage people?

Do you prefer to work as an individual, with a partner or in a team?

Do you like working with your hands?

Do you like solving problems?

Do you have any special skills that could help a team?

Are you a leader or do you like working to other people's instructions?

Working in teams

When individuals work together in a team, sometimes the team can be very effective and sometimes it can be disastrous!

Research by Meredith Belbin has shown that an effective team is made up of a group of people with a wide range of skills. Her method of identifying different types of people and placing them into appropriate groups has been used widely in industry.

According to Belbin, there are three main categories of team role:

- **action-oriented roles** – fulfilled by people who concentrate on the task being carried out
- **people-oriented roles** – fulfilled by people who are good at dealing and communicating with other people
- **cerebral roles** – fulfilled by people who do the thinking!

Let's look at the various types of team member. See if you recognise any characteristics in your friends or even in yourself!

Action-oriented roles

Action-oriented team members concentrate on the tasks being completed. These are more important to them than the people they work with.

Shaper

Someone who thrives on pressure, and has the drive and courage to overcome problems. These people seem to enjoy a challenge and will do anything to reach their goals – nothing seems to stand in their way. They can sometimes offend people by concentrating on the task in hand rather than the people they work with.

Implementer

These people turn ideas into reality. They are disciplined, reliable and efficient, but can be inflexible, and do not like new ideas.

Completer finisher

These people like to complete every last detail and will always get the work completed in time. However, they tend to worry unnecessarily and prefer not to delegate work to others, in case it is not completed.

People-orientated roles

These team members believe that the people involved in a task are very important and that the task will be completed by encouraging the development of good interpersonal relations.

Co-ordinator

A co-ordinator is a confident leader or chairperson, who can identify and clarify aims and objectives. They can comfortably delegate work to team members in order to complete tasks. They are sometimes seen as offloading work to people.

Teamworker

A teamworker is a co-operative and diplomatic team member who avoids friction with other team members. They can waver when an important decision needs to be made.

Resource investigator

These are outgoing team members who make and develop contacts, and explore opportunities. They can be over-enthusiastic and can lose interest soon after the start of a project.

This astronaut has just fulfilled a lifelong dream

A co-ordinator needs to listen carefully to his team

Cerebral roles

These team members are the thinkers and organisers.

They have ideas which they believe will make their team successful.

Planner

These are the creative team members with new ideas and solutions. They can ignore some basic principles and do not always communicate their ideas clearly.

Monitor/evaluator

These team members can monitor a situation, look at the facts and make accurate judgements, but they can lack the character to inspire others.

Specialist

These team members have very specialist knowledge about specific subjects, they are confident and self-motivated but are limited to their area of knowledge.

Many areas of the pharmaceutical industry require specialist knowledge

Consider the different types of team member we have just looked at.

Work in groups of four to five. Agree on which group member is like which of the characters we have just considered.

As a class, make a tally chart of the different characters, for example:

Shaper	III
Implementer	I
Completer finisher	III
Co-ordinator	II
Teamworker	I
Resource investigator	IIII
Plant	I
Monitor/evaluator	IIII
Specialist	II

From now on, try to get a mix of all characteristics in your group when undertaking exercises in groups – this helps to improve team performance.

Writing down the task

Once tasks have been agreed it is important to write all the tasks down and who is to complete which task.

Here we see a simple example of the task broken down. Note that Amy has two tasks; it is usual to have more than one task.

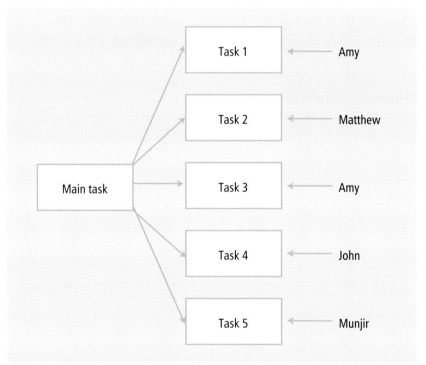

Setting and agreeing individual targets

When tasks have been allocated, it is important that they will be completed on time. There should be a way a measuring how well a task has been completed.

Tasks are often broken down into smaller tasks so that they can be handled more easily.

Agreeing tasks is an important aspect of the allocation of work. If a person is forced to undertake a task, they could have little or no interest in it. Agreeing tasks with team members ensures that they will be motivated and keen to complete the task.

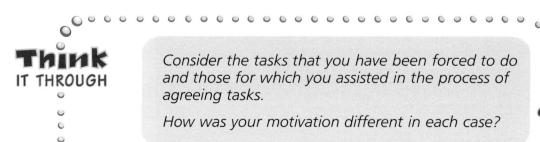

Think
IT THROUGH

Consider the tasks that you have been forced to do and those for which you assisted in the process of agreeing tasks.

How was your motivation different in each case?

Communication

To get the best from a team, good communication is very important.

A relay team must communicate effectively to optimise performance

Communication for design has already been discussed in Unit 1, but it is worth a little revision here.

There are many forms of communication:

- written
  - letter
  - memorandum
  - e-mail
  - online communication such as MSN Messenger or Yahoo Messenger
  - mobile phone text
- verbal
  - instructions
  - discussions
  - telephone conversations
- visual
  - photographs, posters and printouts
  - illustrations
  - graphs and charts
  - websites
  - presentation software such as PowerPoint
- communication aids
  - components
  - music
  - artefacts.

minutes of the meeting
– a written record of exactly what was discussed and agreed at a meeting

Meetings

Information is formally exchanged in business via meetings. The key aspects of a meeting are:

- agenda   (the list of things to discuss)
- attendees   (the people at the meeting)
- chairperson   (the person who runs the meeting)
- secretary   (the person who writes the discussions down; this record is known as the minutes of the meeting)
- identifying actions   (the tasks that need to be carried out)
- any other business   (any issue not on the agenda)
- minutes   (the written record of the meeting)
- distributing **minutes** (giving out a written record of the meeting to members).

Written communication
Letter

These are generally used for external communications with other organisations. It is important to use the correct format, which will show professionalism.

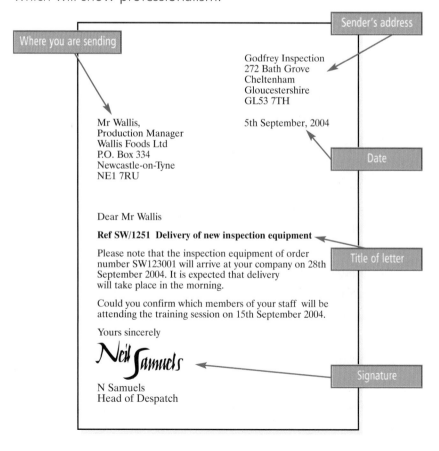

Letters can be kept on file in case of any dispute with an external organisation

Internal memo

These are short written messages. Their main advantage is that they are relatively quickly produced.

Memo

From: Production manager

To: Maintenance manager

Date 20 11 2004

Title: Machine maintenance

Please ensure that Machine 1B has a completed maintence record ready for inspection on Monday 29 11 2004.

A memo can be used to relay a simple instruction

E-mail

E-mail is very commonly used in business. It is a quick way to send and record messages simultaneously. Most managers and office workers have access to e-mail.

It can be used to send photographs, charts and written information.

Online communication

MSN Messenger or Yahoo Messenger are commonly used to hold online conversations. It is possible to conduct multiple conversations at one time, termed a conference. Video conferencing can be employed, using web cams. These systems are used recreationally, but possess some clear advantages when used in a business situation.

Mobile phone texts

Texting on mobile phones is common outside the workplace, but is also capable of getting messages to employees on the move, or over a large business site.

Verbal communication

Instructions

Giving instructions is a basic method of communication; it is crucial to consider the employee's level of knowledge.

Discussions

Small groups discuss issues that arise in a business. This can help to solve problems or to organise events. There may be no need for written documentation, but everyone can agree upon any action that needs to be taken.

Telephone

Telephones are used extensively by businesses. They are easy to use and readily available.

Remember, when telephoning:

- state who you are and which company you are from
- ask clearly for the person or department you would like to be put through to
- be precise about what it is you want to discuss
- do not go into detail until you are directed to the appropriate person (otherwise you may end up repeating yourself).

Visual communication

Photographs, posters and printouts

These are ways of getting a message across quickly. They are used for safety posters, displaying rules and regulations, and advertisements.

Notice boards

These can be used for oddly sized letters, notes and cards. They should be easily visible to people who regularly pass by.

Illustrations and diagrams

Sketches and drawings in support of text or instruction can be very helpful in explaining how things work.

Graphs and charts

Graphs and charts can simplify technical information.

Websites

Websites are now extremely widely used for obtaining information from individuals and companies. They are also used to advertise information about organisations. Producing a website can enable customers to access your business and order products 24 hours a day.

Safety poster

Presentation software such as PowerPoint

Visual presentations on computers and projectors are now widely used. They are becoming much easier to produce. They can be transferred via CD or e-mail, or posted on websites.

Communication aids

When communicating information, supporting elements can be used to get a point across. Music and sound can support or emphasise particular elements of a presentation.

Artefacts and objects

Artefacts are man-made objects. These can be used to assist explanations.

Organisation of communication

Businesses need to decide which method of communication should be used.

They should identify when meetings should take place and who should attend them, and who will need what information and when.

Motivation

A team usually achieves success when all of its members are **motivated**.

If you really want to do something and you are determined to achieve the goals you have set yourself, you are highly motivated.

THE JARGON DRAGON

motivation – eagerness to perform a task

ACTIVITY

People can be motivated in many different ways. Many people work solely for money.

Work in groups. List all the tasks, jobs and activities that you do for free.

This could include:

- sports
- helping people out
- organising events.

You do all these activities for free. List the reasons why you do them.

Complete this sentence . I am motivated by ...

Creating an appropriate working environment

The term 'working environment refers' to the way in which people and communications are organised. There need to be systems in place to ensure that people work together effectively.

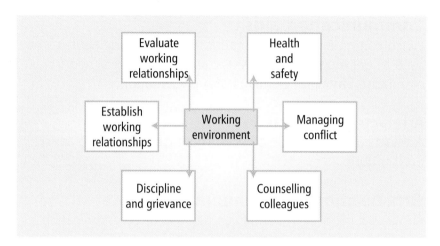

Creating a working environment

Establishing and maintaining working relationships with colleagues

Businesses operate well when there are good relationships between the members of the workforce. Conflicts and disputes can lead to problems in the workplace, which could in turn lead to poor performance.

Some measures can be taken to ensure good relationships with colleagues:

- take time to build constructive relationships
- inform employees about the company's activities
- respect the confidentiality of employees
- deal with conflicts as quickly as possible
- treat employees fairly.

Disciplinary procedures

A system should be in place allowing managers to discipline colleagues.

There are many reasons why discipline could take place.

Discipline can be divided into two main categories: **general misconduct** and **gross misconduct**.

General misconduct

These are minor offences which generally do not harm the business in a significant way, but can lead to worse offences if they are not acted upon.

Examples include:

- being late for work
- using the business's telephone for personal calls
- using a company vehicle for personal journeys
- poor levels of performance.

Gross misconduct

These are offences that are treated very seriously.

Gross misconduct can be one serious act by the employee, or ongoing general misconduct.

Examples include:

- a single act that causes damage to people or the business
- continued lateness
- continued use of the phone for personal use after repeated warning
- continued unauthorised use of a company vehicle after warning
- continued under-performance despite support measures.

An employee's misconduct costs his employer money

Guidance for creating a code of conduct

- Make rules simple so that everyone understands what represents misconduct.
- The rules should be agreed with the employees.
- Ensure that everyone has access to the codes of conduct at all times. (Posters can be used to remind employees.)
- Employees should know what happens if rules are broken.

Sequence of punishment

1 Verbal warning

If an employee is creating some minor problem or nuisance, they will be told verbally.

2 Formal verbal warning

The employee may be given a formal verbal warning, which will be kept on file for a period of time.

3 Written warning

At this stage the employee will be given a written statement of their misconduct, which will be kept on file.

4 Final written warning

The employee will be given a final written warning outlining the seriousness of the warning and notifying them of imminent dismissal if the behaviour continues.

5 Dismissal

The employee is dismissed from the business – this will look bad when they apply for employment in other companies.

Grievance procedures

A grievance procedure is used by employees who have an issue with employers, or with other colleagues in their company.

A grievance procedure helps employees with complaints. It should mean that everyone is treated fairly and quickly.

Complaints could be about any aspect of the workplace that the employee is concerned about, for instance:

- mistreatment by managers or other workers
- bullying
- harassment
- discrimination.

There are four stages to a grievance procedure:

- informal complaint
- first stage
- second stage
- final stage.

Informal complaint by employee

The employee should discuss any problem with their line manager. This is usually the quickest and easiest way to resolve a problem. If this fails, there should be an official procedure to follow.

First stage

The employee should give a written complaint to their line manager. If the complaint is about the line manager the employee should give the written complaint to a more senior manager. They should receive a written response within a set length of time, and an opportunity to have a meeting with a manager to discuss their grievance. They may want to be accompanied by another person so that they do not feel intimidated.

Second stage

If the employee is not satisfied with the outcome of the meeting they can raise a grievance in writing with a higher level of management. They should receive a response within a set time, such as five days. The employee should be told when they will receive a response.

Final stage

If the employee is not satisfied after the second stage, they can write to a higher level of manager, possibly a director or the chief executive. The employee will be given a chance to meet with their manager to discuss the grievance.

Counselling

Support should be provided for employees in a number of areas relating to their personal and professional problems. The level of counselling provided varies from business to business.

Many employers recognise that an employee's performance at work can be affected by other aspects of their lives. Counselling can help the employees, which in turn helps the business.

In general, the larger the business, the greater the support and expertise available. Counselling may help employees with a variety of aspects of their lives, including:

- personal problems
- psychological problems
- financial problems
- family support
- performance problems
- health problems.

A trained counsellor can help employees cope with their problems

Counselling can identify areas in which specialist support and advice would be helpful.

Managing conflict

Conflicts can occur between any members of a business. Conflicts are disagreements between individuals or groups in a business, which could relate to attitudes, beliefs, needs and values. They can involve personal differences or departmental differences. Conflicts can appear suddenly or can run for many years.

There are five steps to managing conflict. These steps are:

- analysing the conflict
- determining how to deal with the conflict
- pre-negotiation
- negotiation
- post-negotiation.

Step 1: analyse the conflict

Try to understand what is causing the conflict. Determine what each party is aiming to achieve and why the conflict has arisen.

Step 2: determine management strategy

Once you have a general understanding of the conflict, the groups involved will need to select the most appropriate strategy for solving the problem. In some cases it may be necessary to include a neutral person in the process.

Conflict management strategies

- collaboration
- compromise
- competition
- accommodation
- avoidance.

Step 3: pre-negotiation

Discuss the reasons for conflict with all parties involved.

Identify what they would regard as a successful resolution of the conflict.

Step 4: negotiation

Concentrate on the needs and concerns of each party. Aim to find options that each party would be satisfied with. When options are drawn up, discussions can then take place about which options are most suitable to resolve the conflict.

Step 5: post-negotiation

Once measures have been agreed upon, it is important that they are seen to be implemented fairly and quickly.

Health and safety in the workplace

Security

There should be procedures in place ensuring that all employees are protected against aggression and violence from other employees.

Safety of materials and equipment

All equipment should have appropriate documentation to show inspection in accordance with safety standards.

Health and safety practice

All hazards and risks should be identified. There should be a procedure for reporting accidents, and one for stopping work if there is a dangerous situation. There will generally be a conflict between production and safety if all production is stopped. It must be clear that safety has priority in these circumstances.

Health and safety guidelines should be clearly displayed in the workplace

Breach of organisational policy

Where the organisational policy of the business is being breached this needs to be recognised and acted upon.

Improvements to health and safety procedure

There should be a system of ongoing improvement to safety. Information about improving safety should be passed to the appropriate person so that new guidelines for safety can be drawn up.

Evaluation of effectiveness of working relationships

There must be a way to ensure that working relationships are effective.

This could be achieved through discussion with employees to get general feedback about the state of relationships within sections of the business.

Appraisals are formal meetings between employees and managers to discuss performance over a period of time, and methods of improving performance, such as training and development. This is an opportunity for employees to discuss working relationships with their colleagues, and how those relationships are affecting their own performance.

Preparation for manufacture

In this section we will look at the importance of preparing for production in a wide range of manufacturing sectors. We will cover many important issues that relate to all manufacturing processes, regardless of sector.

There are two main groups in manufacturing:

- manufacturing sectors
- engineering sectors.

Manufacturing sectors include:

- food and drink
- biological and chemical
- printing and publishing

- paper and board
- textiles and clothing.

Engineering sectors include:

- engineering fabrication
- mechanical and automotive
- electrical and electronic
- computer process control
- telecommunications.

Material preparation

Material should be prepared in accordance with the production plan. It is important to understand the function of each component.

Bought-in parts

When products are manufactured, they will be made up of components that are manufactured by the company, and parts that are 'bought in' already made.

Commonly bought in parts include:

- fasteners (such as nuts, bolts, screws and washers)
- standard parts (such as zips, ink, welding rods)
- basic ingredients (such as flour, sugar, salt)
- threads and fabrics
- buttons
- standard paper sizes.

There are several reasons why parts may be bought in:

- price
- difficulty of manufacture
- speed of manufacture
- difficulty in holding stock
- standardised parts already exist.

Price

When companies manufacture large amounts of a product, the price is often reduced. This is because they can purchase material in bulk, so the overhead costs of the machinery and equipment used to make the product can be shared out.

Difficulty of manufacture

Some components require complicated processes which are not available or too expensive for companies to carry out.

Speed of manufacture

Sometimes it would simply take too long to make the parts required. Often, suppliers hold large amounts of stock and can supply parts very quickly.

Difficulty in holding stock

Parts need to be stored until they are used, taking up valuable space. Modern manufacturing systems enable nearly all of the parts to be bought in and supplied at the last minute.

Manufacturing processes

As we look around us we can see hundreds of products that have been manufactured. It would simply not be feasible to explain how everything in the world was made – you would never get to the end of this book in time to complete your GCSE.

Instead we will look at the popular techniques used to processes metals, polymers and ceramics, before looking in a little more detail at three manufacturing sectors: printing and publishing, textiles and clothing, and food and pharmaceutical processing.

Processing

Before we go any further it is important to understand the term processing, which describes the method of taking a material, component or ingredient, and improving it in some way so that it can be used as a finished product or as part of a larger product.

Processing may involve the casting, forming and shaping, cutting, machining, joining, printing, heating or moulding of a product.

Some finished products contain just one processed part (a paper clip); others contain just a few (a simple pen); others contain a larger number of processed parts and ingredients (a frozen meal); others contain many hundreds of components (a remote control); still others, such as a modern car, combine thousands of parts.

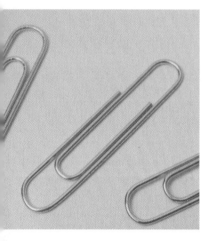

Manufactured products vary in their complexity

Selecting a processing technique

The quality and reliability of any finished product depends heavily on the manufacturing process used to make it – choosing the right process is fundamental to the success of a product. The following are considerations that need to be made before choosing a process.

The type of material, component or ingredient being processed

The properties of a material need to be considered before any manufacturing can take place, to ensure that the material can be successfully processed by the method chosen.

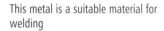

This metal is a suitable material for welding

For example, some metals are very hard and difficult to machine, while some plastics can lose their shape and become soft when heated to relatively low temperatures.

The costs of the processes involved

Manufacturing companies must carefully work out the unit cost of a component by understanding the costs involved in processing.

Processing costs can involve set up costs (purchasing specialist moulds, tooling and the labour required to set up equipment) and running costs (operating and maintaining the equipment), including **consumables**.

THE JARGON DRAGON

consumables – parts, tooling, oils and lubricants which are used up within the manufacturing process

The size, shape and complexity of the product being processed

The size, shape and complexity of a product are always early considerations when choosing the relevant manufacturing process. Some processes cannot involve very large or small products. Alternatively, specialist techniques may be required to achieve the desired outcome – some aircraft turbine parts are so large that they are machined on drills the size of a small house.

In the printing industry, newspapers are processed on large-scale printing presses occupying whole dedicated areas (see the case study), while smaller printing companies producing leaflets may use specialist copying equipment not much larger than photocopiers used in your school or college.

An aircraft turbine
This photograph is reproduced with the permission of Rolls-Royce plc, copyright © Rolls-Royce plc 2004

This machine for making aluminium alloy die castings is aided by computer technology

Many components are too complex to be processed using simple manufacturing methods. For example, many electrical components require computer technology to assist with processing.

The quality required in the final product

Pharmaceutical products, such as headache tablets, must be controlled extremely carefully to ensure that ingredients are processed in accordance with stringent quality guidelines. The processing equipment must be able to maintain these standards – failure to do so could obviously result in the possibility of producing a dangerously defective product.

Some products that are pressed or formed may require a secondary process to improve quality characteristics such as surface finish – the primary process may simply not be able to produce the required standard. Forging is a process often used to produce car parts, such as crankshafts, which in some cases require further machining to improve dimensional accuracy.

The amount of product being processed

This issue is closely related to price, in that some processes require a relatively large volume of product to become economical.

An example is injection moulding (used for the processing of many plastic parts). This process is initially very expensive to set up, and is generally used only when large batches of products are required, i.e. 10 000 units or more. It would be too expensive to set up this type of process if only a few units were required – in this case, an alternative process would need to be used.

The computer technology required

Many modern manufacturing processes use computers to assist with the processing of materials, components and ingredients. Common examples are computer aided manufacturing (CAM) and computer integrated manufacturing (CIM). Both of these innovations are described in more detail in Unit 3: Application of technology.

Computer technology can assist the manufacturing process by producing high quality products at low cost, reducing cycle times from design to manufacture, and reducing waste material.

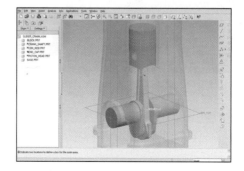

A CAM image of a piston

Environmental concerns

Manufacturing processes generally produce scrap and waste material in addition to the finished product.

Some byproducts of manufacturing are harmful to the environment, causing air and water pollution, acid rain, the hole in the ozone layer, the greenhouse effect and global warming.

Waste products from industrial processes can harm the environment

The safe disposal, recycling and treatment of waste material are now governed by stringent international laws.

These themes are discussed in a little more detail within Unit 3: Application of technology.

Techniques used to process metals

As discussed previously, metals are naturally occurring elements which can be loosely grouped into one of two broad categories – ferrous (those containing iron) and non-ferrous (those without iron). You may also remember that 'alloy' is a term used to describe a combination of two or more metals.

A ferrous alloy

The physical properties of gold change when it is melted

All the considerations we have just discussed are important, but when selecting a production method for a metal material, perhaps the most significant factors are the physical properties of the metal or alloy, i.e. strength, hardness, toughness, etc.

Metals are very versatile and can be formed at room temperature when warmed slightly, or at high temperatures: the physical properties change with the temperature.

Steel, for example, becomes much softer at higher temperatures, which is why blacksmiths heat horseshoes before hammering them into shape.

Some metals are very hard and tough, making them difficult to cut and machine, while others are very soft, making them easy to shape at room temperature.

The following section introduces the common processes used to form, shape and machine the group of materials known as the metals.

Casting

Casting is among the oldest techniques used to form metal products. It dates back thousands of years to the production of basic tools and weaponry, such as arrowheads.

Casting has lasted so long as a processing technique because it can be used on the majority of metals, producing complex products in one single piece. Often the quality of the cast product is so high that no further finishing process is necessary.

Casting involves three main stages:

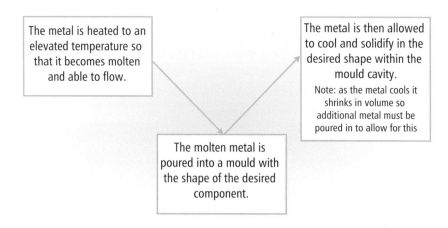

Stages of casting

The metal is heated to an elevated temperature so that it becomes molten and able to flow.

The molten metal is poured into a mould with the shape of the desired component.

The metal is then allowed to cool and solidify in the desired shape within the mould cavity.

Note: as the metal cools it shrinks in volume so additional metal must be poured in to allow for this

There are many different types of casting techniques (too many to be described here), which can be classified into two broad groups: expendable mould casting and permanent mould casting.

Expendable mould casting

This type of casting process uses a mould that cannot be re-used once the part has solidified. The mould is destroyed to free it from the part. Moulds are consequently made from cheap **refractory** materials, able to with stand high temperatures, such as sand or plaster.

Two common expendable mould casting processes are sand casting and investment casting.

Sand casting

Sand casting uses a mould made from sand, containing a hollow cavity in the middle shaped like the finished part.

The type of sand used is called green sand. Green sand is specially mixed, including additional clay and water to help it bind together and retain its shape.

The main advantages of sand casting include the capacity to produce parts of any size (so long as you have enough sand!) and low costs, because the sand can be reused.

Typical parts made by sand casting include cast-iron engine blocks, machine beds and very large propellers for ocean liners.

The stages of sand casting are as follows.

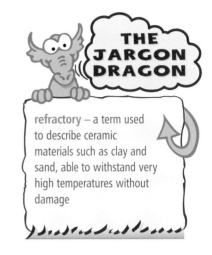

THE JARGON DRAGON

refractory – a term used to describe ceramic materials such as clay and sand, able to withstand very high temperatures without damage

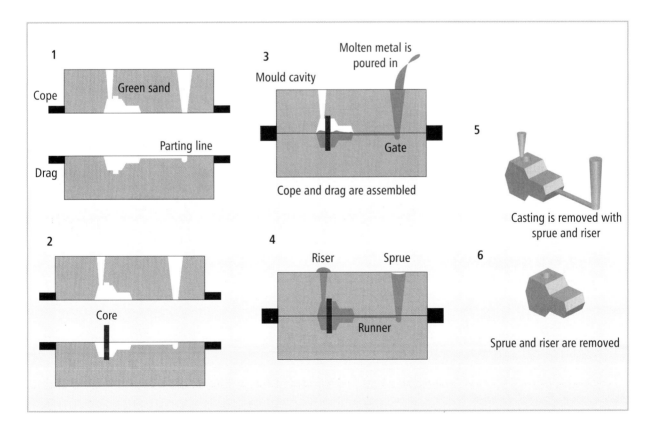

A pattern is produced in two halves (usually from wood, plastic or metal) in the shape and size of the desired finished part.

The pattern is split into the two halves and placed within two moulds – the cope is the top mould; the drag is the bottom mould.

The green sand is then placed carefully around the pattern to surround all the features. It is then pressed down.

After the mould has been shaped, the pattern is removed to reveal a cavity in the sand. The two halves (cope and drag) are closed, clamped, and weighted down to prevent the mould from separating under the pressure exerted when the molten metal is poured into the mould cavity.

The molten metal is poured into the mould; once it has solidified, the mold is opened and the part removed from the sand.

Molten aluminium being poured into a mould

Investment casting

Investment casting is an expendable mould casting process used to make products such as gears, cams, turbine components and some parts for office equipment.

The investment process is also known as the lost wax method. It involves making a pattern from wax or plastic by injecting the liquid material into a metal **die**.

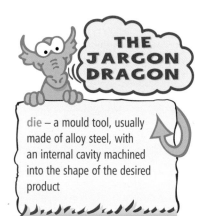

THE JARGON DRAGON

die – a mould tool, usually made of alloy steel, with an internal cavity machined into the shape of the desired product

Once solidified, the pattern (which will be used to make the mould) is removed from the die and dipped in a slurry of ceramic material, such as very fine silica, and a binding material which helps to hold it together.

Following this initial coating the process is repeated to increase the layer thickness of the mould.

The one-piece mould is then dried and heated, removing the wax or plastic (and any residual water), but leaving the ceramic mould in one piece.

The metal is then poured into the mould. After the metal has solidified, the mould is broken up and the casting can be removed.

It is common for individual moulds to be joined together, forming a 'tree'.

Labour and material costs make the lost wax process expensive; it is suitable for casting high-melting point alloys with a good finish and close tolerance. Thus little or no finishing is required.

Other commonly used expendable moulding processes include plastic-mould casting and shell-mould casting.

Use the Internet to find out how these processes work.

FIND IT OUT

Permanent mould casting

Permanent mould casting uses a mould that can be reused. The moulds are made from metals able to retain their shape at high temperatures – steel alloys for example.

The mould is made in two halves with a cavity machined into the middle. It also incorporates a way of adding the molten metal – commonly called a gating system.

The two halves of the mould are brought together, clamped and heated to an elevated temperature, allowing the molten metal to flow and cool consistently.

Upon solidification, the part can be removed. Sometimes specially integrated pins are needed to release complex parts.

Common types of permanent mould casting processes include centrifugal casting and die casting – the latter is discussed in a little more detail on the next page.

Die casting

Developed in the early twentieth century, the die casting process is an example of permanent mould casting.

The two main types of die casting can be classified as gravity (whereby only gravity ensures the metal flows into the mould cavity) and pressure casting (whereby the metal is applied under force).

Both involve the application of molten metal into a die, which can be separated into two or more pieces to remove the solidified product.

Typical components made by this process include hand tools, toys and motors.

A gravity die casting workstation producing aluminium fan cases

Forming

Forming operations are those in which the shape of a metal piece is changed by subjecting it to an external force. Forging, pressing, rolling and extrusion are all types of forming techniques.

Many metals can be formed in this way as long as they are ductile enough and capable of being permanently shaped without cracking or fracturing.

When the metal is formed at elevated temperature, the process is termed **hot working**; otherwise it is known as **cold working**.

With most of the forming techniques, both hot and cold-working procedures are possible.

Forging

Forging simply involves hammering a piece of metal into a desired shape. The metal is generally heated to ensure it becomes soft and more **malleable**, at which point a force is applied through a large industrial hammer.

In most cases two dies are used: one is applied to the top of the metal **billet**, the other beneath it; hence the part is formed by its position in the middle of this high pressure sandwich.

Hand tools, railway parts and automotive crankshafts are all formed using this technique.

THE JARGON DRAGON

malleability – the ease with which a material can be hammered into shape

billet – a piece of material, ready for processing, often pre-prepared

This industrial forge has a 7-tonne hammer

Rolling

Rolling, the most widely used forming process, consists of passing a piece of metal between two rolls.

As the metal passes through the rolls it is reduced in thickness.

Cold rolling may be used in the production of sheet, strip, and foil metal with high quality surface finish. Other shapes can be achieved by using specially machined rolls – steel beams and railway tracks are made in this way.

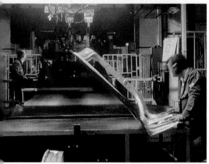

Extrusion

In this process, a bar of metal is forced through a die; the extruded piece emerges with the same shape as the die.

Parts made via extrusion include rods and tubing.

Sheet metal forming

Sheet metal forming is used in manufacturing to produce products such as car doors and bonnets, oil drums and soft drink cans.

A piece of sheet metal is fed into special equipment which presses it into the required shape. Normally this is done at room temperatures, so the metals formed in this manner need to be relatively ductile – mild steel is commonly used.

Techniques used to process polymers

Polymer materials are well known to us as food containers, computer parts and children's toys. In fact it's hard to look around these days and not see a polymer product.

The two types of polymer materials are plastics and rubber materials (sometimes called elastomers).

Plastics have a wide range of different properties. Some are hard and rigid, others are soft and flexible. A very useful property is insulation, i.e. they are poor conductors of heat or electricity.

Polyethylene (used for plastic bags), polypropylene (traffic cones), PVC (window frames) and polystyrene (foam packaging) are all examples of well-known plastics.

Plastics materials might be either thermoplastic or thermosetting; this is always a major factor when choosing a method of forming. Another consideration is the temperature at which a plastics material softens enough to be formed successfully, which is normally elevated.

Moulding

Moulding is by far the most common method for forming plastics. The process involves heating up pellets of a plastic material and forcing them into a mould so that they then adapt the shape of the carefully prepared space inside.

The most popular moulding techniques include compression, injection and blow moulding, discussed in more detail on the next page.

Other processes you may wish to investigate include rotational moulding, casting and extrusion. Plastics are cast and extruded in very similar ways to metals.

Compression moulding

Compression moulding can be used for both thermoplastic and thermosetting plastics. It involves placing a precise amount of plastic material between two halves of a mould. Both pieces of the mould are then heated and brought together, squeezing the plastic into shape.

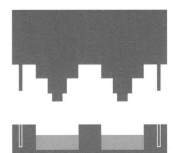

With compression moulding two halves of a mould are heated and brought together

Injection moulding

Injection moulding is the plastics equivalent of the metal die casting process. It can be used for thermoplastic and thermosetting polymers.

The process is quite complex, yet relatively simple to understand – plastic pellets are loaded into a hopper and stored until the correct amount of plastic material needed to make the component is heated to a liquid and forced into a mould under pressure.

Once the plastic has cooled and solidified into the desired shape, the mould comes apart, releasing the plastic component.

The mould closes and the process is repeated over and over again.

An injection moulding machine

This is an extremely quick process, capable of producing parts every 10 seconds. However, the process is generally reserved for products produced in high volumes (10 000+) because of large set up and tooling costs.

Components made using this process include car parts, models, toys, electronic components and food containers.

Blow moulding

Blow moulding is a process used to make hollow plastic parts such as bottles or food containers. It is similar to the process of making glass bottles.

First the plastic material is heated and formed into a tube: this freshly produced tube is placed into a mould while still hot.

The final component is formed by blowing air or steam into the mould, which forces the plastic tube out, taking the shape of the mould cavity. The mould then comes apart, freeing the finished part.

Techniques used to process ceramics

The most popular ceramic materials used in manufacturing are glass and clay products. These are typically used as windows, food and drink containers, tableware and ornaments.

Ceramic materials are generally difficult to process because they are very hard and very brittle. Processing methods such as forming and machining can be readily applied to plastics or metals but would usually cause ceramic materials to crack or fracture.

Some ceramic materials such as glass are formed at high temperatures, allowing the materials to become molten. In this molten state the product can be formed into shape. Materials made from clay can be formed into shape by mixing with a liquid such as water.

Other ceramic materials are formed from powder, which must be heated in an oven to make the product hard, rigid and stable. This technique is used to make electronic components such as resistors and capacitors (see Unit 3: Application of technology).

Processing glass products

If you take a quartz crystal, grind it up into fine sand, mix it with some soda, add limestone, and then heat the lot up, you will find yourself making a hard, transparent material – we call it glass.

The following briefly describes the methods of processing glass products.

Pressing

Pressing is used to make tableware products such as cups, plates and dishes. The raw materials are heated to an elevated temperature and then pressed into shape using a specially shaped mould.

Drawing

Drawing involves heating up the materials to an elevated temperature until they become molten. The materials are then fed through hot rollers which form the glass into rods, tubes and sheets.

Blowing

Blowing is used for producing jars and bottles. It involves taking a measured amount of molten material and placing into a mould. An insert is then used to press the material roughly against the mould wall, at which point the insert is removed and compressed air is introduced to form the finished part.

Clay forming

Clay is often mixed with materials such as flint and quartz to make various products such as tableware. These materials are often ground to fine powder, at which point they are mixed with water. The addition of a liquid allows the material to flow adequately, which facilitates forming or casting.

Two techniques to form clay products are hydroplastic forming and slip casting.

Hydroplastic forming

Hydroplastic forming uses materials that are very pliable and easy to shape without cracking. Building bricks are formed by forcing the material through a die which forms the shape – this type of forming is called extrusion. The product must then be heated in an oven or kiln to evaporate the water, making the material very hard and brittle.

Slip casting

Slip casting also involves mixing the materials with water, but in this case the mix must be even more runny or fluid. The mix is fed into a porous mould; the excess water then drains through the mould leaving the clay material behind. Depending on the thickness of the finished piece, the process can be repeated until the mould is full, or until the wall thickness of the product is achieved – the latter involves turning the mould upside down so that the extra material can drain away.

Machine tools used to process materials

There are several basic machine tools that are not used in mass production but that can be used for manufacturing metal products in machine shops. They are very versatile and can be used to make many complicated engineering products.

Machine tools include:

- centre lathes
- vertical and horizontal milling machines
- drilling machines.

Centre lathes

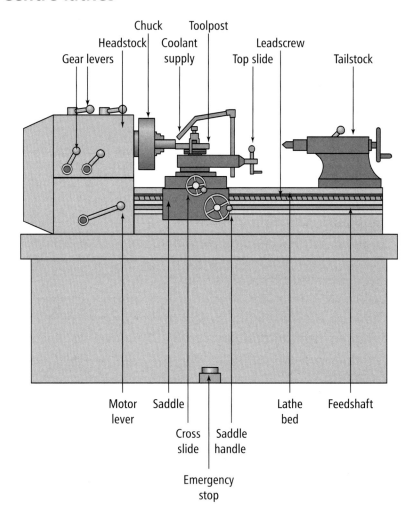

Centre lathes are widely used in industry. These machines produce cylindrical shapes as the work piece revolves around its own centre. A **tailstock** sits at the back of the lathe bed. **Chucks** and **drills** can be put into the tailstock. The centre of the drills will be at the same height as the centre of the work piece.

Tools that that cut the work piece will also be at the same height or on centre. The centre lathe is so called because everything revolves around the centre of the work piece.

Centre lathes are normally very accurate, but, as with all equipment, their accuracy depends on how well the machines are maintained and the quality of the cutting tools used. If the cutting tool is worn, it will not be as accurate.

The work piece is held in a chuck specially designed to hole round bars. The chuck revolves and the cutting tool is moved into a position where it can cut the revolving work piece.

The process of using a lathe is known as **turning**. A craftsman who is specially skilled in the use of centre lathes is known as a **turner**.

There are several important things that need to be considered when using a centre lathe.

Type of turning tool

The turning tool is held in the tool post. The shape of the turning tool will determine the type of finish, the form of the work piece and how much material can be removed.

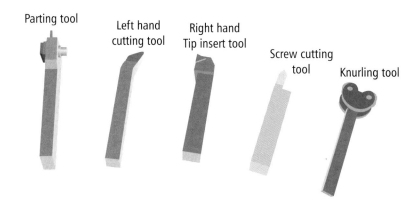

Types of turning tool

Turning tools can be left-hand tools or right-hand tools. These cut in opposite directions. If we hold a right-hand knife tool in our right hand the tool moves in a clockwise direction.

Tools may need to be thin to cut grooves. Sometimes a groove needs to be so deep that it cuts through the work piece, causing the work piece to drop off. This process is known as **parting off** and uses a **parting tool**.

Operations

Many operations can be performed on a centre lathe, which can be categorised as follows.

Parallel turning

This procedure will remove material from the work piece to reduce the diameter. The diameter will be the same all the way along the length.

Facing off

When the work piece has been sawn, it will have a rough edge. This process moves the tool across the front face of the work piece, 90 degrees to the length of the shaft.

This process can be used to make sure that all faces and shoulders are at 90 degrees to the shaft.

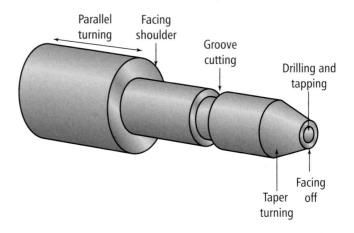

The results of typical turning operations

Taper turning

When a work piece needs a smaller diameter at one end, a taper can be turned. For short tapers, the cross slide is moved to the angle required. As the cross slide hand wheel is revolved, the cutting tool moves along the work piece and cuts a taper.

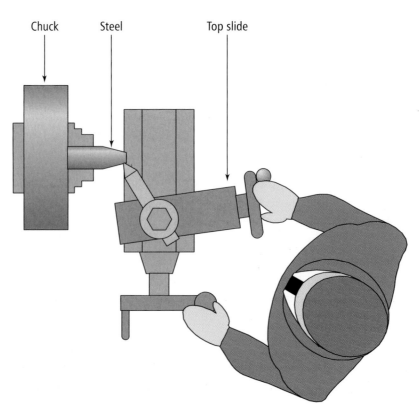

Drilling

The centre lathe has the facility to drill holes. The tailstock sits on the back of the lathe bed. Drills can be paced into a small drill chuck. The tailstock is moved near to the work piece by unlocking the quick release lever and held firmly in place. A hand wheel is then rotated, moving the drill bit into the work piece.

The depth of hole is read from a scale on the tailstock.

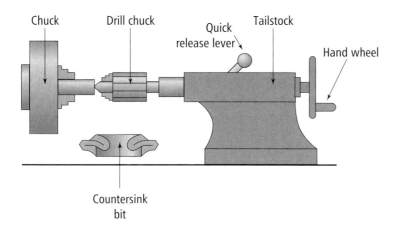

Knurling

When a grip finish is needed for products such as handles or hammer shafts, a process known as knurling can be used.

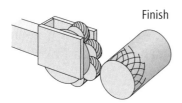

A knurling tool has two rollers with teeth formed in the surface of the rollers which are forced onto the surface of the work piece as it revolves. The result is a grip texture that has a pattern of small diamond shapes cut into the work piece.

Milling machines

Milling machines are used widely in industry. They are generally large. The work piece is held in a **machine vice** which sits on a work table. The work table is moved left to right, forward and backwards, and upwards.

A cutting tool revolves but stays in the same position. As the work piece moves past the cutting tool, material is cut from the work piece.

The accuracy of milling machines depends upon the quality of the cutting tool and the care taken to maintain and clean the machines. Milling machines can be vertical or horizontal, depending on whether the spindle and the cutting tool are in a vertical or horizontal position.

Vertical milling machines

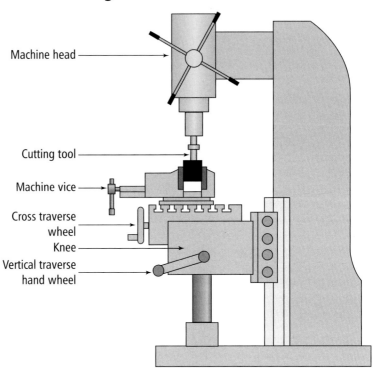

The vertical milling machine is used to cut slots, square edges, shoulders or holes.

Cutting tools can come in a variety of different forms, each of which will produce a different cutting profile.

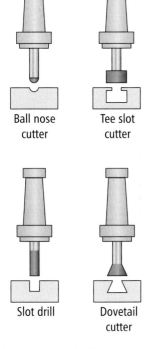

A range of vertical milling cutters (left)

Typical vertical milling operations (right)

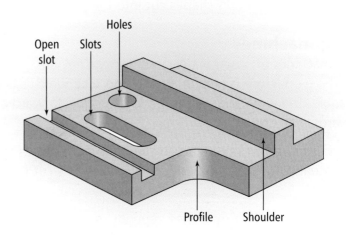

Horizontal milling machines

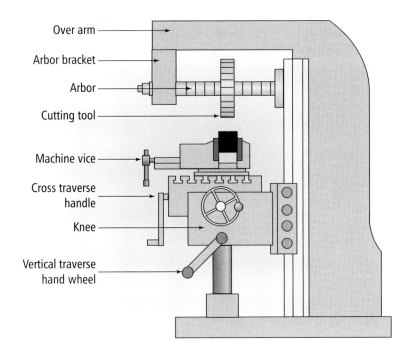

The cutting tool on these machines rotates on a horizontal spindle known as an **arbor**.

These machines have limited use but are very effective at producing slots or key ways.

Cutting tools can be grouped together on the arbor; this is a very efficient way to produce work with a continuous profile or cross-section.

A range of horizontal milling cutters

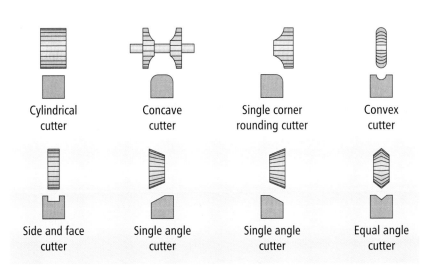

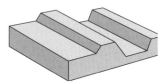

Cutters can combine together to create profiles

Horizontal milling cutters can create chamfers and radii on the edges of work pieces. They can also produce flat bottomed, V-shaped or radiused grooves on work pieces.

Drilling machines

Drilling machines are extremely common in engineering workshops. Their role is to produce holes in work pieces. There is no accurate way to move the work piece once it is clamped, so marking out the work piece is extremely important.

There are two types of machine drill: the bench drill and the pillar drill.

The bench drill

Bench drills are secured to the top surfaces of work benches or specially produced frames. They have limited adjustment of the height of the table. They can operate at a range of speeds so that differently sized holes can be drilled. They are smaller than pillar drills, and generally less expensive, which means that they are often used in workshops at home.

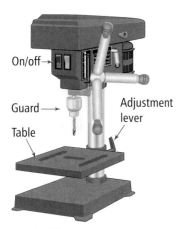

A bench drill

Pillar drills

Pillar drills operate in the same way as bench drills. However, the table can be adjusted to move almost to the floor, as it is attached to a pillar.

This allows larger or taller work pieces to be drilled. Generally pillar drills are much more robust, rigid and powerful than bench drills, so can drill bigger holes.

Drilling tools

Drilling machines use **twist drills**. Twist drills come in standard sizes from 0.5 mm up to 13 mm, to be used in a drill chuck.

As twist drills become bigger in diameter, a morse taper is used to hold the twist drill directly into the spindle of the drill.

Twist drills held in place by a morse taper are released using a drill drift and mallet.

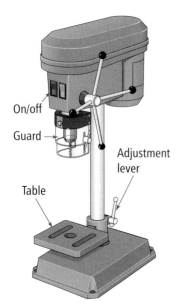

A pillar drill

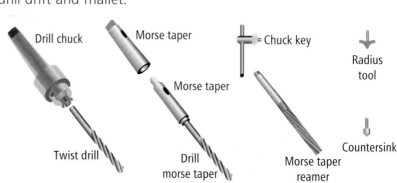

Drilling tools (right)

Counter sink

A counter sink produces a chamfer leading in to a hole, after the hole has been drilled. It is used so that countersunk screw heads lie flush with the surface of the work piece. The size of the chamfer depends on how deep the countersink is pushed into the hole.

Counter bore

A counter bore drills a second hole over the drilled hole at a set depth, allowing the screw head to sit below the surface of the work piece.

Spot face

This is where a slot drill cuts a round flat surface onto the work piece, so that fasteners such as washers or screw heads can tighten onto a flat surface.

Centre drills

Centre drills are used to give a lead into bigger drills. When a small hole is needed, a centre punch indent is enough to align the drill. When larger holes are needed, a centre drill creates a guide hole big enough for the drill to follow.

Work holding devices

When work pieces are machined, they need to be held securely.

Here are some questions that will help to decide which device to use.

Where is the work piece to be held:

- on a work bench
- on a centre lathe
- on a milling machine
- on a bench or pillar drill?

What is the shape of the work piece:

- round or cylindrical
- square or flat
- odd shape?

Bench vice

A bench vice is generally used on work benches in the workshop. They are strong and sturdy, so can withstand the wear and tear of the workshop. They are very heavy, but weight is not important as they are not moved from place to place. They are not very accurate, but are perfect for hacksawing and filing.

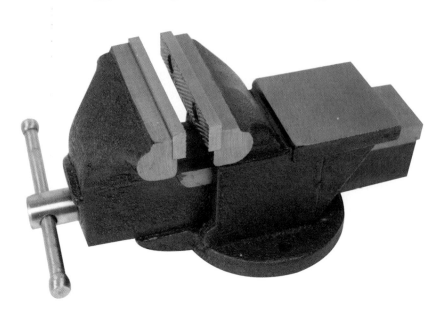

Bench vice

Hand-held vice

A hand-held vice is used for holding work pieces on a bench drill or pedestal drill, if holes are very small. These vices are designed to withstand the downward pressure of a drill as the work piece rests on a surface. There are usually slots in the base where clamps can hold the vice if necessary. Clamps are used when the holes to be drilled are large, and the forces involved are therefore also large.

Hand-held vice

Milling vices

Vices for milling machines are always clamped to the work table, as milling machines are very powerful. The jaws that hold the work piece are flat and accurate. A handle is needed to tighten the work piece. The vice could be a fixed type which cannot rotate, or universal type, which can tilt to an angle or rotate.

Fixed milling vice

Universal milling vice

Focus on paper and card production

Paper and card are used commonly throughout the developed world. Although primarily used for communication and packaging, paper and card have thousands of other uses. You might expect that electronic communication and the internet would force paper out of fashion, but in fact demand is increasing.

We will consider the following important areas relating to paper and card:

- the paper industry
- the history of paper
- what is paper
- types of paper
- pulp
- paper production
- paper recovery and re-cycling.

The paper industry

The industry is growing rapidly, owing to high demand for the media, and the needs of offices and food packaging.

This 45 tonne reel of paper is ready to be slit into smaller lengths

The whole process of producing paper and card creates and maintains many jobs and involves local businesses in foresting, pulp manufacture, the production of paper and card and the recycling process.

THE JARGON DRAGON

capital expenditure – money spent on the machinery and plant

In towns, local newspapers may employ hundreds of people, and in the countryside forests need to be managed by local people. Paper and board mills often have recycling departments which recover and re-use paper.

The industry has a high **capital expenditure**. The European paper industry has nearly half a billion tonnes of newsprint machinery, valued at hundreds of million of pounds.

History of paper

Paper has been around for hundreds of years but its production increased suddenly around 1800 AD. There were five main stages in the history of the paper industry.

THE JARGON DRAGON

web – a length of paper supplied on a roll, which means that printing can be continuous

1 **1800–1860:** the process became mechanised.
2 **1840–1860:** more rag substitutes were introduced, including groundwood pulp and chemical pulp, on an industrial scale.
3 **1860–1950:** the **web** width increased. Improvements in technology and the advent of electricity led to an increase in working speeds. New machines were made for specific paper grades.
4 **1950–1980:** better automation meant even faster speeds and wider webs. New pulps, recovered paper and fillers were introduced. Companies specialised in types of paper. Companies merged or closed unprofitable plants.
5 **1980–future:** better sheet forming principles and chemical pulp processes are being developed. Global markets continue to grow The increased use of computers is increasing demand for paper.

What is paper?

Paper is made by breaking down wood into pulp and extracting the tiny cellulose **fibres**. These fibres are made into flat sheets of various thicknesses, with millions of uses.

Types of paper

Some papers are coated in minerals such as china clay or calcium carbonate. If the paper is to be used for writing it is not coated.

Paper can be bleached or unbleached, depending on the use of the paper. If the paper is used for newsprint or packing, the paper is not bleached.

Paper can be broken down into five main types:

- newsprint and magazine papers
- writing and printing papers
- household papers and sanitary papers
- paper-based packaging
- specialised papers.

Newsprint and magazine papers

Made from **mechanical pulp**, this paper has a density of about about 40 to 60 grams per square metre, and is **machine finished**, usually off-white in colour. Newsprint is used in reels for letterpress and offset printing.

THE JARGON DRAGON

fibres – tiny threads or filaments that form the basis of larger materials (in the paper industry, they are extracted from wood)

THE JARGON DRAGON

mechanical pulp – wood that has been broken down by machines and mixed with water to form a soggy mixture from which paper is made

THE JARGON DRAGON

machine finished – paper that is ready to be used from the machine

The paper used for newspapers is made from mechanical pulp

Magazine paper is better for printing graphics because of the better surface finish. It contains less mechanical pulp than newsprint; it uses pulp which is broken down with heat and chemicals.

A separate section on printing starts on page 177.

Magazine paper has a glossy surface finish

THE JARGON DRAGON

coated papers – papers with a special coating which allows them to be printed upon

Writing paper
This is uncoated woodfree paper, where 90% of the fibre furnish is made up of chemical pulp fibres. Finishing processes can be used to finish paper. These include sizing, calendaring, pigmenting, coating and watermarking. The products made from this paper include office stationery and computer printer paper.

Printing paper
This paper is coated with chemicals such as calcium carbonate to allow printing on the surface. Printing papers are known as **coated papers** for this reason.

Household papers and sanitary papers
If you look around your own home, you will see examples of this type of paper: kitchen towels, tissue paper and toilet tissue. The **parent reel stock** is made from **virgin pulp** or **recovered fibre**, or in some cases of mixtures of both.

THE JARGON DRAGON

parent reel stock – the original roll of manufactured paper

virgin pulp – pulp made directly from trees

recovered pulp – pulp made from recycled paper

Paper-based packaging

Case materials fall into this category; that is, paper and board mainly used in the manufacture of corrugated board.

Specialised papers

There are many other applications of paper products including those used by the building industry, such as insulating boards or plasterboard.

Pulp

Paper is made from pulp, which is wood that has been broken down with water, heat or chemicals.

Pulp can be made from a mixture of woods, recycled paper, or in fact any byproduct of wood, such as sawdust, or trees that have been thinned out of a forest to allow the growth of other trees. This is both good for the environment and cost-effective.

Pulp can be classified into two types, according to when it is sold. It is important to understand the difference between these types. **Integrated pulp** is the term for pulp that is sold to another part of the same paper mill. If the pulp is sold to outside customers, or if it is exported, then it is known as **market pulp**.

The logs on the left are on their way to a paper factory, where they will get turned into pulp (below)

Grades of pulp

There are various types of pulp, based upon how the pulp is made and what it is made from. The variations are known as pulp grades.

Pulp grades are classified firstly by the category of wood – softwood or hardwood – secondly by the processes used to manufacture the pulp – chemical, mechanical or heat (thermo) – and thirdly by whether the pulp is bleached or unbleached.

There are four types of pulp:

- mechanical pulp
- semi-chemical pulp
- chemical pulp
- de-inked pulp.

Mechanical pulp

This type of pulp is ground by wheels into short fibres which are mainly used to produce newsprint paper. Pulp made in this way is known as **stone groundwood pulp**. When steam is used to soften the wood before processing, the pulp is known as thermo-mechanical pulp or TMP.

Semi-chemical pulp

The wood can be softened by chemicals before processing and refining, producing what is known as semi-chemical pulp. This is used for lighter papers such as household and sanitary papers. Combining thermo, chemical and mechanical processes yields chemi-thermo mechanical pulp (CTMP). This pulp is used for printing and writing grade paper.

Chemical pulps

Some pulps are treated with chemicals in a pressure vessel at high temperatures. The chemical will affect the grades of paper produced. Chemical pulps include sulphur pulp and sulphate pulp.

De-inked pulps

A lot of recycling is involved in the paper and pulp industries. Harmful inks and dyes must be removed in the recycling process: this is known as de-inking.

Forestry

Wood is renewable and recyclable: hence it is an extremely useful natural raw material. Forests have many functions, as well as producing wood for pulp production and building, including:

- supporting wildlife
- converting carbon dioxide into the oxygen that we breathe
- employment
- recreation
- education.

The Forestry Commission
The Forestry Commission is the government department responsible for setting the policy on forests in the UK. Its commissioners are appointed by the Queen. The Secretary of State for Environment, Food and Rural Affairs is the cabinet minister responsible for forestry in England.

Certification of forests
To ensure that the paper industry's raw materials are managed effectively and are sustainable, forests are certificated. The UK woodland assurance standard (UKWAS) certifies forests that meet set standards, via the independent assessment of forest management.

In the UK, there are over one million **hectares** of forest certified by UKWAS, and about the same area of uncertified forest.

THE JARGON DRAGON

hectare – an area of 10 000 square metres

Trees as raw materials
Wood is the main raw material for pulp and then paper. It contains cellulose fibre. It can be harvested throughout the year.

Different trees are used for different paper products, for example:

- paper making trees (softwoods)
  spruce
  pine
  larch
  fir
  cedar
- paper and card making trees (hardwoods)
  birch
  aspen.

THE JARGON DRAGON

properties – characteristics of materials, such as strength and weight

Paper manufacturers will blend or mix different woods to produce a grade of paper or card with the **properties** that they desire.

The papermaking process

Raw materials

There are two main fibrous raw materials used in papermaking: wood pulp and recovered paper. Wood pulp is made from wood, whereas recovered paper has been recycled.

Additives in the papermaking process include

- natural mineral fillers
- dyes
- chemicals
- water.

Wood pulp is supplied to the paper mill in the form of thick sheets.

Recovered paper is supplied in large, compressed blocks known as bails.

These are broken down in vessels called pulpers so that the fibres they contain are separated from each other. Water is added, multiplying the original weight of the wood by up to a hundred times. Steel rotor blades cut and break up the raw material, resulting in a runny mixture known as slurry or papermaking stock.

The slurry is sent to holding tanks where chemicals are added to reduce ink and water penetration.

Common additives are:

- clay
- chalk
- titanium dioxide.

The papermaking stock is then pumped through mechanical cleaning equipment to remove any ink or dirt, before being pumped to the **paper machine**.

THE JARGON DRAGON

paper machine – the machine that takes papermaking stock and produces paper on a web

The wet end of a paper machine – pulp is passed through the machine to extract water

The important features of a paper machine are its web producing width (from 1 m to 10 m wide) and the speed at which paper is made, which can be as fast as 100 km/h.

More water is added at the paper machine, turning the slurry into a viscous liquid with only a few parts fibre to 1000 parts water. This liquid passes through the head-box and is squeezed through a long thin slit, throwing the solution onto a moving wire mesh frame up to 6 metres wide.

Sheet formation takes place as the water is sucked out of the solution and paper becomes visible: this is known as a web.

The web is squeezed through a series of rollers to remove most of the water. Then the paper is dried by being heated to over 100°C. The web is supported by fabric belts to prevent it from breaking.

At this stage the paper is complete and wound onto reels. It may undergo further operations depending upon its specification.

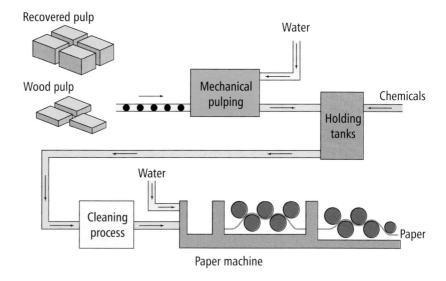

Processes involved in making paper

Paper finishing operations
There are four stages to paper finishing.

1. Calendering – the paper is rolled between metal rollers to smooth its surface.
2. Slitting – the paper is cut into thinner rolls.
3. Coating – chemical or clay coatings are added to enable printing.
4. Wrapping – the paper is wrapped to protect it from the environment as it travels to the customer.

Recycling paper

The process of recycling paper is relatively easy compared to other materials, and is a major part of paper production. Paper has been recycled for centuries. Today, newspapers, cardboard, packaging, stationery, mail, magazines and catalogues are all recycled.

In most towns paper waste is collected in separate boxes or bags on refuse collection day.

Here we see where recycled paper comes from:

You can help the environment by recycling all your newspapers

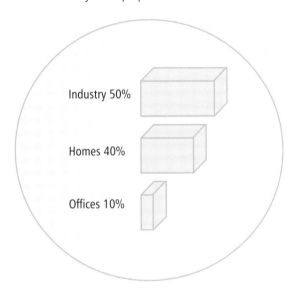

Industry 50%

Homes 40%

Offices 10%

Sources of recycled paper

The recycling process

Fibres originating from new pulp are known as virgin fibres. Fibres originating from recycled paper are known as recovered paper fibres.

The process of recycling paper is similar to producing new paper, but much more cleaning is required.

The main processes are as follows:

- paper is collected
- paper is sorted and graded
- paper is delivered to a paper mill
- recovered paper is slushed into pulp
- non-fibrous parts such as staples are removed
- fibres are cleaned
- ink is removed from the paper (this is only needed for some paper grades)
- pulp is filtered.

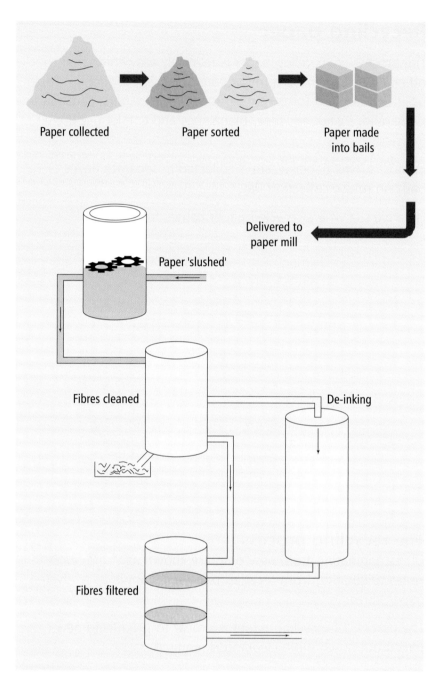

Paper collected → Paper sorted → Paper made into bails

Delivered to paper mill

Paper 'slushed'

Fibres cleaned

De-inking

Fibres filtered

The process of reclaiming paper

De-inking

De-inking is needed only for some paper types, such as hygiene papers. Ink contaminating the pulp of reclaimed paper will cause the paper not to be white, so the ink is removed, a process known as de-inking.

The fibres are dissolved in water to form a slush, and then washed with detergents. When air is blown into the mixture, the ink attaches to the bubbles and rises to the top. This is known as the floatation process. Hydrogen peroxide is sometimes used to bleach the fibres.

Focus on the printing and publishing industry

In a modern world dominated by the Internet, we could be forgiven for thinking that paper images are on the decline, but in fact physical products need to be printed more than ever. This section looks at the industry that provides us with the many magazines, books, stationery and newspapers we use every day. Printing is the process of transferring text or pictures onto a **substrate**.

THE JARGON DRAGON

substrate – the substrate is the material being printed upon, e.g. paper or card, among others

The main parts of a printing process

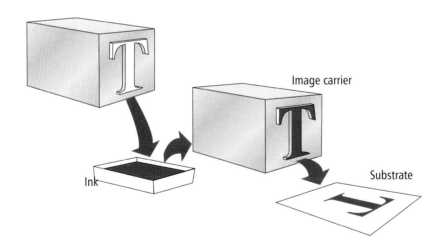

Image carrier

Ink

Substrate

The drawing above shows a simplified printing process. This section examines more closely the different techniques and methods used commonly in industry today.

Take a look around and list all the products you think have been printed.

- How many could you find?
- List the things that are substrates.
- What were the materials used to make the substrates?

Ink

Ink is a runny fluid that comes in many different colours. When it is mass-produced, it must dry quickly, because some chemicals can be harmful. Therefore ventilation is strictly controlled.

Image carriers

The image carrier is a physical component on which the image is cut, burnt or machined.

The image carrier is often, but not always, in **mirror image**.

mirror image – a reversed image

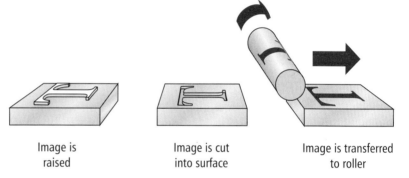

Image is raised

Image is cut into surface

Image is transferred to roller

ACTIVITY

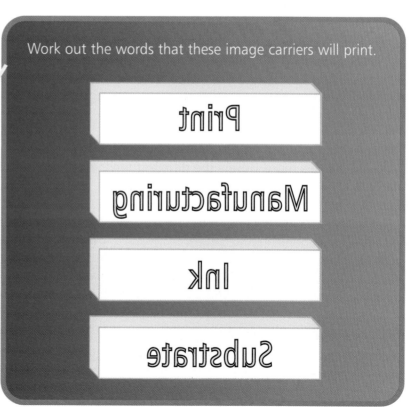

Work out the words that these image carriers will print.

Print

Manufacturing

Ink

Substrate

Answers on page 321

Substrates

Substrates are the products that are printed upon. We see paper and books every day, but printing directly onto components is often more cost-effective, because it saves money in buying labels or stickers, or cutting images directly into the product.

The material used to make the substrate is an important factor, as is the type of ink: the ink must complement the substrate. Particular processes are suited to particular substrates.

Preparing the image

In most cases the customer will supply the image to be printed to the printing company – this could be a digital image or a photographic image. Images can be captured by a range of devices, such as a camera, scanner or computer.

A **proof** is prepared to check for position and accuracy. The proof should be checked by the customer to ensure everything is as it should be.

Printing in colour

Full colour images are usually produced by a process known as four-colour printing, as four basic colours can be used to produce almost any image.

The four colours used to produce any colour image are:

- cyan
- **magenta**
- yellow
- **black**.

The four different colours that are used to print this image in full colour are shown above, right

Four colour process printing is commonly used to print books, magazines and newspapers (see the case study on page 298).

Methods of printing

Let's take a look at the main types of printing processes used in the modern printing sector:

- offset lithographic printing
- letterpress
- gravure
- screen printing
- flexography
- digital printing.

Offset lithographic printing

Lithography is known as an offset printing technique. It involves printing on paper and card.

Products printed using offset lithography include:

- newspapers
- magazines
- books
- stationery.

Offset lithography is used to print a range of everyday items

THE
JARGON
DRAGON

rubber blanket –
ensures the correct
transmission of ink to the
surface of the print medium

Offset lithographic printing process

The ink is not applied directly from the printing plate (or cylinder) to the substrate. Ink is applied to the printing plate to form the image which is then transferred or 'offset' to a rubber blanket. The image on the blanket is then transferred to the paper or card.

The paper or card can be fed in sheets into what is called a sheet-fed press, or on a roll known as a web into a web-fed press. Lithographic plates are the cheapest printing surfaces available, making this process very popular.

Making lithographic printing plates

The aluminium plate has a thin surface coating of light-sensitive material, such as a photopolymer. When the surface is exposed to blue or ultraviolet light, its solubility changes.

Images are transferred to the surface by exposing the plate through a film. The film is placed over the aluminium; light is passed through it so that the areas not covered by black film change solubility.

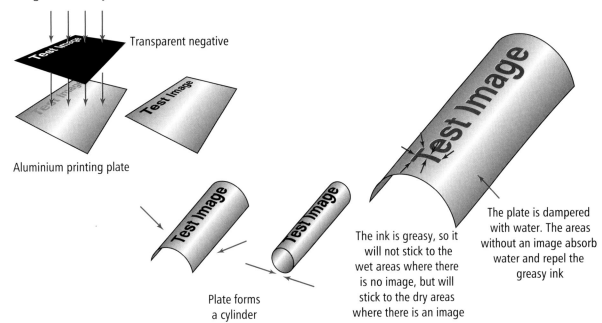

Transparent negative

Aluminium printing plate

Plate forms
a cylinder

The ink is greasy, so it
will not stick to the
wet areas where there
is no image, but will
stick to the dry areas
where there is an image

The plate is dampered
with water. The areas
without an image absorb
water and repel the
greasy ink

Offset lithography has a wide range of applications, from small sheet-fed machines to large machines that produce magazines and catalogues.

On **sheet-fed presses**, the paper is fed into the press, one sheet at a time, at very high speed. **Web-fed presses** always print on a continuous roll of paper or card, before the paper is cut to size.

Heatset and non-heatset printing

Sometimes the ink is dried using heat: this is known as heatset printing. It accelerates the printing process, as drying time is reduced. When more than one colour is being used the ink of one colour must be dry before the next colour is applied – this prevents the colours 'bleeding' into one another.

The plate cylinder rotates and is dampened by rollers. Some areas absorb the water and others repel it.

Ink is transferred to the plate cylinder: where there is water on the cylinder, the ink is repelled. At this point we see the image in ink.

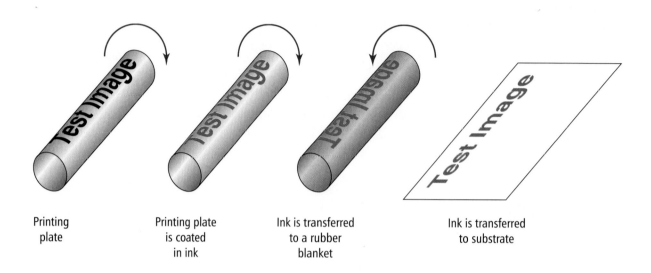

Printing plate

Printing plate is coated in ink

Ink is transferred to a rubber blanket

Ink is transferred to substrate

The inking rollers then transfer the ink to the dampened plate, the ink will only adhere to the image areas.

The inked image is transferred to the rubber blanket, and the paper is printed as it passes between the blanket and impression cylinder.

There are three basic lithographic press designs:

- **Unit-design press** – a self-contained printing station made up of a plate cylinder, a blanket cylinder, and an impression cylinder. Two or more stations may be joined to perform multi-colour printing.
- **Common impression cylinder press** – consists of two or more sets of plate and blanket cylinders sharing a common impression cylinder. This allows two or more colours to be printed at a single station.
- **Blanket-to-blanket press** – contains two sets of plates and blanket cylinders without an impression cylinder, enabling the paper to be printed on both sides at once.

All offset presses have three printing cylinders, as well as the inking and dampening systems: the plate cylinder, the blanket cylinder and the impression cylinder.

The main operations in lithographic printing are as follows:

- preparing the image
- processing the printing plates
- printing
- finishing.

Offset lithographic inks

There are several types of inks used in offset lithographic printing, for instance:

- petroleum based
- vegetable oil based
- ultra-violet and electron-beam curable
- heatset.

Letterpress printing

Offset letterpress, often simply called letterpress, is the oldest method of printing. Equipment and images are printed by relief printing plates, whereby the image or printing areas are raised above the non-printing areas.

Faster methods of printing, such as offset lithographic printing or flexographic printing, have largely replaced letterpresses. Set-up time is relatively long which means that long print runs are required and image carriers are expensive to produce.

Typically, letterpress printing is used for:

- business cards
- letterhead proofs
- posters
- imprinting
- embossing
- hot-leaf stamping.

Letterpress printing uses three main methods:

- sheetfed platen
- sheetfed flatbed
- rotary webfed.

Examples of embossing

Methods of letterpress printing

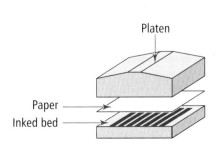
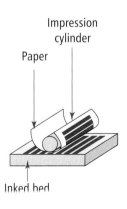
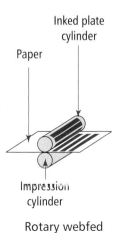

Sheetfed platen   Sheetfed flatbed   Rotary webfed

Sheetfed platen letterpress

The substrate, usually paper, is placed in the press. An image carrier with a raised printing area is then pushed onto the paper held in place by the **platen**.

Sheetfed flatbed letterpress

The paper is fed into the press; the impression cylinder creates force on the paper over the raised image on the image carrier. Prints can measure up to 1000 mm by 1400 mm. The rate of production, around 5000 prints per hour, is relatively slow, so the method is used less frequently these days.

Rotary webfed letterpress

A continuous sheet of paper, known as a web, runs through two cylinders. The inked plate cylinder carries the image; the impression cylinder creates the pressure. Some new presses can print up to six pages across a 2 metre web.

Making the letterpress image carrier

The text to be printed is laid out or set on a wax casting, which is then coated in graphite and placed in a special chemical (electroplating) bath.

A coating of copper forms around the wax casting, creating a strong, durable letterpress plate.

Preparation of letterpress printing plates

Letterpress printing uses relief type, raised above the non-printing areas.

Like all rotary presses, rotary letterpress requires curved image carrying plates. The most popular types of plates are:

- stereotype
- electrotype
- moulded plastic or rubber.

The gravure process

The main type of gravure printing is called rotogravure, which uses a web press and a cylindrical image carrier. Rotary sheet-fed gravure is used to make high quality prints such as banknotes, and can be used to print on thin films and plastics.

Producing the plates for gravure printing

Gravure plates are made from copper, with a chrome plated surface to increase their service life. The cylinder can range from the size of a tin of tuna to 6 metres long by a metre in diameter.

Products printed using gravure printing

Gravure printing is used for long run, high quality printing, producing a sharp, fine image. It can be used for:

- food packaging
- wallpaper
- wrapping paper
- furniture laminates
- panelling
- magazines
- certificates
- money.

Banknotes are printed on a gravure press

Gravure printing process

The first part of the process involves etching an image into the plate, which is then applied to the plate cylinder. As the engraved image passes through the ink, the grooves are filled with ink. As the plate rotates, it comes into contact with the substrate, and the ink is transferred to the substrate – in this case, web-fed paper. The doctor blade is used to wipe excess ink from the plate cylinder, leaving only the ink in the etched grooves.

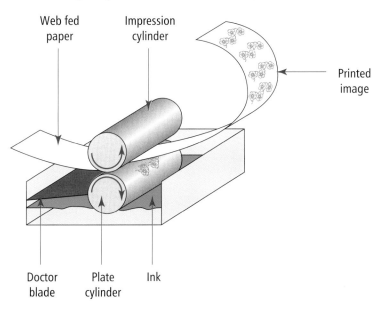

Web fed paper

Impression cylinder

Printed image

Doctor blade

Plate cylinder

Ink

Screen-printed t-shirts

Screen printing

Screen printing is very versatile. It can be used to print on a wide range of substrates, on any shape or thickness. The ink can be much thicker than that used in other processes, so it can produce some great effects and textures. The simplicity of the process means that a wider range of inks can be used.

Substrates include:

- paper
- paperboard
- plastics
- glass
- metals
- textiles
- printed circuit boards.

Screen printing consists of four elements:

- the screen
- the screen frame
- the squeegee
- ink.

There are two types of screen printing presses:

- flat-bed
- cylinder.

The flat-bed screen printer

A porous mesh or fabric is stretched over the screen frame. The screen frame may be wood or metal.

Flat-bed screen printing

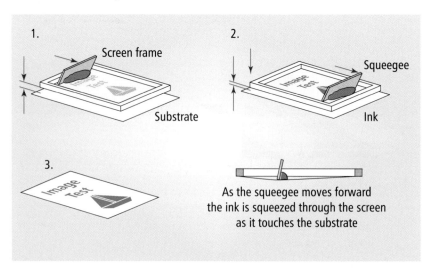

A stencil is produced on the screen by using a coat of ink-resistant emulsion, preventing the ink from passing through onto unwanted areas of the substrate.

The squeegee pushes the ink across the surface of the screen and the ink permeates through to the substrate. The printed product is then sent to a drying oven or **UV curing system**.

THE JARGON DRAGON

UV curing system – a special oven which uses ultra violet light to help the ink dry

Screen printing can produce 25 000 impressions without wearing out the image.

Cylinder screen printing

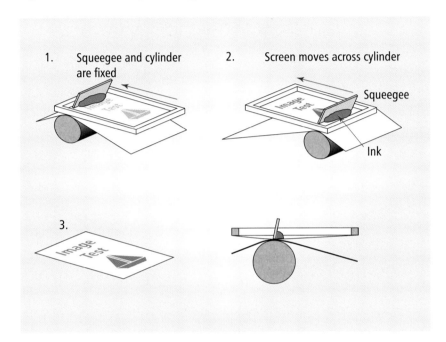

Cylinder screen printing

Before screen printing takes place:

- the customer provides photographs and text to be printed
- the image is converted into a positive image
- the image is processed onto the screen fabric
- the screen is mounted onto a screen frame.

Flexographic printing

Flexography is the main printing process used to print packaging materials.

Products printed using flexography include:

- corrugated containers
- folding cartons
- paper sacks
- plastic bags
- milk cartons
- wrappers.

Flexographic printing products

Flexographic printing process

In flexographic printing, the substrate is fed into the printing press from a roll.

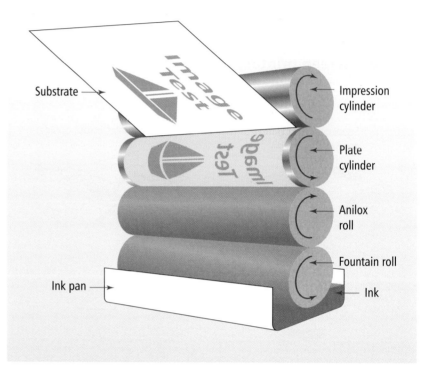

The process of flexographic printing

The flexographic printing system uses four-colour printing to produce complete photographic pictures. The image is printed as the substrate is pulled through a series of print units, each of which prints one colour only.

The anilox roll inking system is vital in this printing process.

Millions of tiny cells are engraved into the ink meter roller, which transfers ink from the ink pan to the plate. The volume of ink transferred to the plate depends on the size of these tiny cells. The ink around the cells must be removed as the anilox rotates.

Flexographic plate making
Plates are made using a relief method, whereby the printing area is higher than the non-printing area. The plates are flexible, made from either plastic or rubber.

Flexographic inks dry quickly, which is important, owing to the high speed at which printing takes place. The inks also have low viscosity. The inks sit on the surface of non-absorbent substrates, and solidify when solvents are removed.

Plate-less processes
The growth of modern digital printing methods means that the image carrier, usually a plate, does not have to be made. Digital information identifies where ink should be applied to the paper

A flexographic printing press

or substrate, reducing the lead time needed to produce a print. Some examples of these plate-less processes are listed below:

- ink-jet printers
- laser printers
- impact printers (dot matrix)
- dye sublimation printers
- plotters.

Ink-jet printers

Sometimes called bubble jets, ink-jet printers work by spraying drops of ink onto the page. The image is formed by using magnetised plates to direct the ink onto the page. Print densities range from 300 dots per inch upwards.

Laser printers

Laser printers compare favourably to other printers in terms of speed, quality and reliability. They burn an image onto a drum which passes through small particles called toner. Electronically charged parts on the drum attract the toner, which is then transferred to the paper using heat and pressure.

Impact printers

Also known as **dot matrix printers**, impact printers use tiny pins packed closely together. The pins press onto a ribbon containing the ink, which in turn then presses onto the paper.

Impact printers are poor at producing graphics or good quality print, but are cheap and efficient, so they are used in many offices where lots of documents need to be completed quickly. They are mainly used on carbonised forms, where up to five pieces of paper can be printed at once.

Dye sublimation printers

Used for high quality professional printing, they work by individually laying down the four main colours – yellow, cyan, magenta and black. There are no dots (as in ink-jet and laser printers), so the images have near perfect quality. A disadvantage is that the paper is expensive, because the colours have to diffuse into the surface.

Plotters

Plotters are large printers that can print on up to A0 size paper. They are used for technical or architectural type drawings, such as building plans, which are required to be quite large.

The two basic types of plotters are:

- **flatbed plotters**, which are horizontal, resembling a table. The paper is held in place; special pens automatically draw the image onto the paper
- **drum plotters**, which use paper that is rolled over a cylinder as the ink cartridge moves over the paper. These printers are preferable to flatbed printers because they take up less room and can produce larger drawings.

Transfer pad printing (pad printing)
The main elements of the pad printing process are:

- the printing plate
- the ink
- a silicone rubber printing pad
- a doctor blade or ink cup
- the machine.

The image carrier is usually a steel or hard plastic plate with the image burnt or etched into the surface.

The ink covers the plate. A doctor blade wipes the excess ink away, leaving a pool of ink in the shape of the image.

Solvent in the ink evaporates, changing the consistency of the ink from runny to sticky.

When the silicon pad is pushed over the ink, it adheres to the sticky pad. The pad moves to a component and is pushed onto it. The ink leaves the pad, transferring the image to the product.

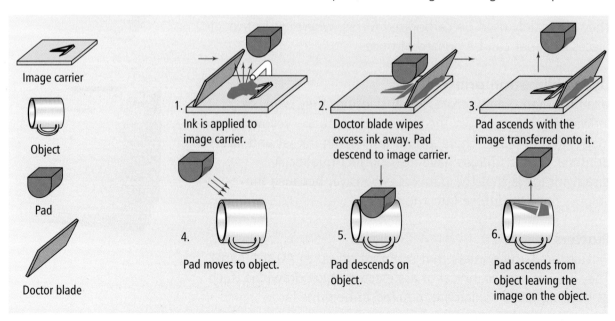

Image carrier

Object

Pad

Doctor blade

1. Ink is applied to image carrier.

2. Doctor blade wipes excess ink away. Pad descend to image carrier.

3. Pad ascends with the image transferred onto it.

4. Pad moves to object.

5. Pad descends on object.

6. Pad ascends from object leaving the image on the object.

Focus on the textile industry

In order to make any clothes or garments, a raw material is required. In the textile industry, the raw materials are the cloth or **fabric** that is used. Fabric is made from lengths of material that we would recognise as cotton or wool. These lengths are known as **yarn**.

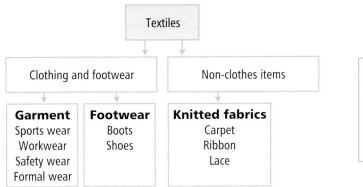

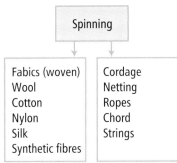

Some of the main fabrics used today are:

- wool
- cotton
- nylon
- silk
- synthetic fibres.

Wool

Wool features in the wardrobes of most people, in the form of a winter pullover. However, wool can also be very lightweight and thin.

THE JARGON DRAGON

yarn – a strand of manmade or natural fibre used to make garments by knitting or weaving

fabrics – interwoven yarn that generally appears like cloth. It can be made from animal coats, silkworm cocoons or plants

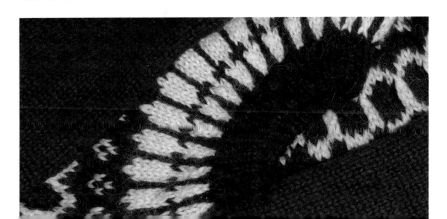

Wool offers protection from the cold winter months

There are five steps in the manufacture of wool:

- shearing
- sorting and grading
- spinning yarn
- making fabric
- finishing.

Shearing

Sheep naturally produce a woolly fleece every year to protect themselves from cold winter weather. This fleece is removed by a professional shearer in the spring when the warmer weather arrives. The best quality wool originates from the shoulders and sides of the sheep.

Shearing can be difficult when the sheep wriggles around

Look at this web site:

http://www.chesterfarms.com/shearing_sheep.htm for a great demonstration of sheep shearing.

Sorting and grading

Poor quality wool is removed from the fleece. The fibres are then sorted into different grades, according to criteria such as strength, fineness, waviness (crimp) and colour. The wool is cleaned, removing all dirt, and then **carded**, a type of combing process that untangles the fibres and creates a flat sheet called a web.

Spinning yarn

Roving is converted to yarn on spinning frames. Once spun, the defects in the yarn are removed during the winding process.

There are two main types of yarn: worsted wool is lighter and smoother than woollen yarn but needs more processes to manufacture. Products made from worsted wool can be light and smooth, and allow perspiration.

Making fabric

Wool manufacturers knit or **weave** yarn into a variety of fabrics. Wool can be hand-knit or processed on large automated machines.

Dying

Woollen yarn can be dyed in dyeing kettles, which look like large baths.

Wool may also be dyed at various stages of the manufacturing process and undergo finishing processes, depending on the customer's specification.

THE JARGON DRAGON

carding – converts loose wool to a fine, even web, which is then divided into long, continuous strips called roving

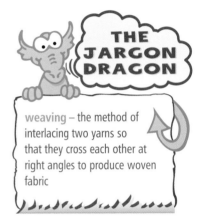

THE JARGON DRAGON

weaving – the method of interlacing two yarns so that they cross each other at right angles to produce woven fabric

Dyeing kettles

Balls of dyed wool

Finishing fabrics
Fulling
The finishing of fabrics made of woollen yarn begins with fulling. The fabric is soaked in water and passed through rollers, causing the fibres to interlock as the fabric shrinks.

Crabbing
Crabbing is used only on worsted wools. The fabric is submerged in hot water, then in cold water, strengthening the fabric.

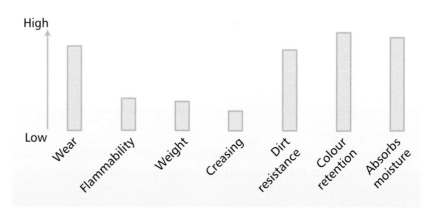

Properties of wool

Cotton

Cotton is a soft white fibrous substance produced naturally from the seeds of certain plants.

Cotton manufacture
Raw cotton is fed into **cleaning machines** and **picking machines**, where the cotton is mixed and broken into smaller pieces, and dirt is removed.

The fibres are separated in a **carding machine**. The cotton goes through a comber which can remove shorter fibres, giving the cotton strength.

During the spinning processes:

- the cotton is reduced to smaller structures
- the fibres are straightened
- the yarn is twisted.

The yarn is then made into fabric by weaving or knitting.

The fabric is checked and passed over a flame to de-fuzz the cloth, and is then bleached in hypochlorite or peroxide.

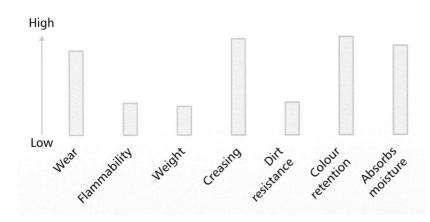

Properties of cotton

Uses

Cotton is used to make:

- clothing
- shirts
- shorts
- jackets
- curtains.

- denim jeans
- household goods
- pillowcases
- carpets

Nylon

Nylon is a synthetic (manmade) polymer developed by scientists in New York and London – hence the name. It has many uses as a plastic material but is also used to make fabrics.

To make nylon a fabric the molten material is forced through small holes in a spinneret. This creates lengths of soft nylon which harden into fibre as they cool. They are then wound onto spools.

The fibres are unwound from the spools and stretched which gives the nylon increased strength. When this process is complete the nylon is twisted and wound onto a further spool.

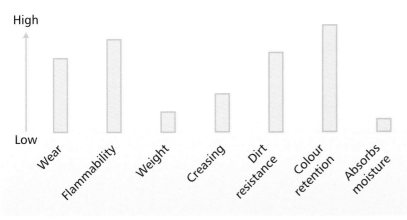

Properties of nylon

A nylon umbrella

Uses

Nylon is used to make:

- tracksuits
- hosiery
- shorts
- swimwear
- umbrellas.

- tents
- bed covers
- parachutes
- sportswear

Silk

Silk is naturally produced by the cocoons of silkworms. These worms are farmed in an environment that allows the silk to be removed.

High quality garments are made using manual processes such as hand wheels and looms to produce silk. Mass-produced silk is unwound by modern manufacturing machines.

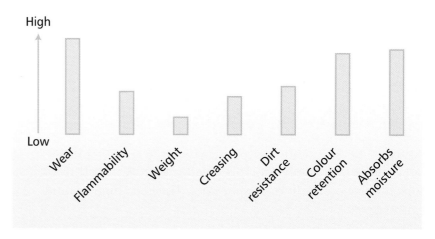

Properties of silk

Silk is smooth and shiny

Uses

Silk is used to make:

- dresses
- scarves

- ties
- curtains.

Polyester

Polyester is the name given to a range of manmade textiles. They are made from chemical substances generally found in petroleum. The polyester fibre, most commonly polyethylene terephthalate (PET), is used to make fabrics.

Polyesters are manufactured in three basic forms:

- fibres
- films
- plastics.

PET is made via a complex chemical process carried out at high temperature in a vacuum. The material is extruded. PET is often made from recycled products to save money and energy.

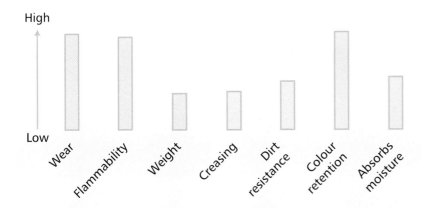

Properties of polyester

Uses
Polyester is used to make:

- shirts
- running shorts
- lingerie

- tracksuits
- tents
- sports bags.

Textile and clothing waste

Recycling textiles and fabrics
Recycling fabrics not only saves the process of making the clothes but also the process of making the textile in the first place. The easiest way to recycle textiles is to give them to charity shops. However, clothes can be used as cleaning rags or filling material, or the actual fibres may be re-used to make new yarn. Whichever way textiles are re-used, it makes good sense to save time, money and energy!

Polyester trousers

Clothing manufacture

Clothing, like food and shelter, is a basic need for all people, but there is so much more to modern clothing than meets the

THE
JARGON
DRAGON

corporate identity – logos,
clothing or documentation
that helps us identify a
business

eye. It is no longer just a way of keeping warm and dry: it has become a way of expressing individual identities and **corporate identities**.

Examples of clothing that help us
identify businesses

Clothing types

There are so many different types of clothes that we need to categorise them into groups. This list shows some of these groups:

costumes	pants
dresses	pyjamas and nightwear
equestrian	rainwear
footwear	safety wear
headwear	shirts
hosiery	sportswear
lingerie	suits
medical	sweaters
motorcycle wear	swimwear
neckwear	tee-shirts
outer wear	vests.

ACTIVITY

It would take a long time to mention every type of garment manufactured, but consider the list above. Are there other groups of clothing product that you think could be added to the list?

Processes involved in clothing

Clothing manufacturers need to consider the full range of processes involved in making clothes.

Design
This gives all the dimensions and details of the product to be made. Designs provide enough information to make a prototype.

Renderings
Rendered drawings can be sketched or produced on CAD systems. They can be sent by post, fax or email to show clients a general view of what the product will look like.

Conceptboards
These are sketches with explanations of why a particular part of the product looks as it does, which may relate to customer demand, fashion or existing styles.

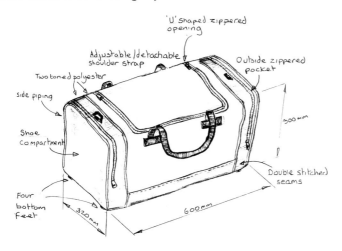

Product art direction
This is the process of producing photographs or illustrations to help market the product, for magazines, catalogues or websites.

Brand analysis
This involves looking at existing brands to ensure that new products will be of similar style, and that customers who like a particular brand will desire the new product.

Fashion copywriting
This process produces drawings or images for marketing and newsletters. It helps to name a brand and describes the terms associated with the product.

Retail store planning

Products are not simply placed in a shop or outlet with a hope that they will sell. Shop displays are designed to give the customer the best view of the products.

Can you think of new clothing products that have been launched?

In small groups, discuss the brands and products that have had the greatest hype before they even appear in shops. Here is a list of areas that you might consider:

- trainers
- jeans
- fashion wear.
- sportswear
- football boots

Garment silhouettes

Silhouettes are simplistic diagrams of clothes laid flat to show the outline shape, a good method of choosing clothes and styles. They are often used on website catalogues because they are simple to understand.

Printing

Spot prints and all over prints can be used to vary the style of products. **Pattern prints** have a repeated pattern which covers the garment.

THE JARGON DRAGON

silhouette – a plan view of a garment that gives a quick indication of colours and styles

spot print – a type of print that repeats itself in a pattern to cover a large area

pattern print – a large print which covers the whole garment

Use the following website to find example of silhouettes and spot prints:

http://www.apparelsearch.com/Apparel_Search_2.htm

In small groups design a spot print for a tee-shirt. Use a graphics package such as Paint Shop Pro or Adobe Photoshop to help with your designing.

Garment production

Manufacture of a jacket

Consider the processes involved in manufacturing a suit jacket.

Suit jackets can range from a made to measure one-off suit to a mass-produced product made to standard sizes. Type of product and quality control may vary, but the principal manufacturing stages are the same.

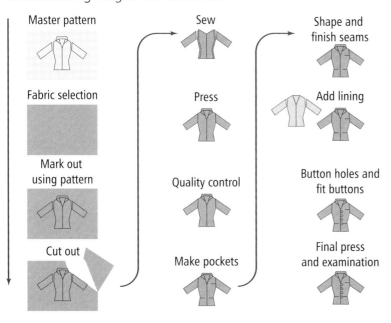

A simple outline of the processes used in the manufacture of a suit jacket

1 Pattern making

When a design is complete, a master pattern maker will produce a master pattern. Copies of this, called working patterns, are used to mark out the cloth to be cut.

2 Fabric selection

The most appropriate fabric for the customer's needs is selected. Selection is based upon weight, colour and pattern, or any other aspect that is specified. The details will be in the product specification to meet the customer's design brief.

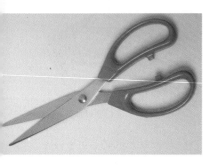

3 Marking out

The garment is marked out using a working pattern. Any lines or pattern in the fabric must be marked in the correct direction.

4 Cutting

A master cutter cuts out the garment and makes sure that stripes are perfectly matched.

5 Sewing

This can be done by machine or by hand, depending upon the quality of suit needed. The quality of the stitching is important to the overall quality of the garment.

6 Pressing

Suits can be pressed dozens of time during manufacture, not only to eliminate creases and flatten the material, but also to give the suit its shape. The higher the quality of suit, the more pressing it will require.

7 Quality control

At this stage the main parts of the jacket have been assembled. Inspection takes place to ensure that seams, cutting and pressing have all been carried out to the standards required. There would be no point proceeding beyond this stage if the garment was incorrect.

8 Pocket making

The top and side pockets are cut and linings added. Supports can be added at this stage to strengthen pocket openings.

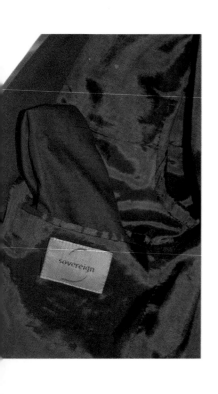

9 Shape and finish seams

Edges of the seams are cut and trimmed to give the jacket a good fit. The level of work done at this stage will depend upon the quality required.

10 Lining

Linings are fitted to the jacket and sewn in place. As with the main outer jacket, the quality of the lining will depend upon the specification of the jacket.

11 Button holes and buttons

Button holes and buttons are cut and edges sewn to give the hole durability.

Buttons are bought in from different departments, or from suppliers. They are stitched in place with a gap between the button and jacket, known as a shank. This will allow the button to free from stress in the fastened position.

12 Final press and examination

The final press gives the jacket its final shape and flatness.

The final inspection of a jacket involves checking seams, pressing, shape, and stitching. The level and amount of inspection will depend upon the specification of the jacket. Inspecting a single suit of the highest quality can last for hours.

Sewing

Sewing is the main way in which fabrics are joined together. Sewing can join flat sheets of fabric, sleeves and collars, and produce seams.

Seams

Seams are the joints that hold the fabric together. There are many different types of seam, as shown below:

4-thread overedge seam

3-thread overedge seam, wide and narrow

Zigzag lockstitch

2-needle bottom coverstitch

4-needle 6-thread coverstitch

3-needle 5-thread coverstitch

5-thread safetystitch

Single thread blindstitch

3-needle bottom coverstitch

3-thread flatlock, wide and narrow

3-thread overedge

Sewing machines

Industrial sewing machines are more powerful and faster versions of household sewing machines.

There are two main parts to the machine:

- the sewing machine itself
- the power stand.

Sewing machines can operate at around 2000 to 5000 revolutions per minute (rev/min) with a powerful motor. Pulleys are used to increase the number of stitches per minute (spm).

Household sewing machines can do zigzag and straight stitching. Industrial machines are faster and more consistent in their quality. Household sewing machines operate at 500–800 spm: they are restricted in speed by the size of their motors.

High speed lockstitch machines perform one operation at a time.

Classification of machine

Terms such as semi-industrial, heavy duty and industrial strength are sometimes used to advertise household sewing machines. Generally these terms give the impression of power, which can be misleading.

Sewing machine types

Overlock sewing machines and lockstitch sewing machines are both used in industry.

Overlock sewing machine (left) and lockstitch sewing machine (right)

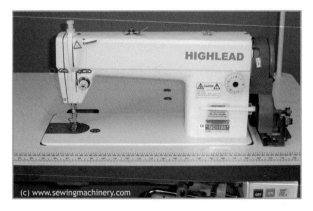

Sewing machine maintenance

- Clean lint from tension mechanisms and bobbin areas – lint left in these areas can destroy machine parts.
- Use the manufacturer's recommended oil for sewing machines. The manufacturer's manual will say exactly where to oil the machine.

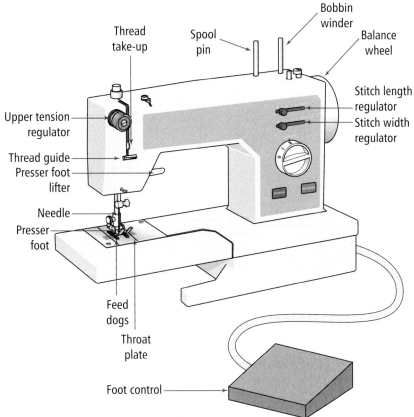

- When a sewing machine has been oiled, sew two pieces of cloth together to test for leakage, which could ruin a garment.

Oil has a number of roles, including to:

- help lubrication
- prevent rust
- extend the life of the sewing machine.

Other material joining processes
Materials can be joined by other processes. Some materials are waterproof, so stitched holes could leak. Special joining systems are used to join rubbers or polymer-coated fabrics.

Welding seams
Textiles such as polymers or coated textiles are often welded together using high frequency machines or hot air. This creates excellent seams.

Joining rubber-coated textiles
In order to form seams for waterproof clothing or fashion clothing, rubber-coated fabrics can be **heat vulcanised**, which ensures a strong seal.

Focus on the pharmaceutical industry

The UK pharmaceutical industry is a successful high-technology industry. It is very competitive and has a trade surplus of over two billion pounds. This country's pharmaceutical industry is ranked as one of the three most profitable in the world.

The Association of the British Pharmaceutical Industry (ABPI) is the trade association for about a hundred companies in the UK which produce prescription medicines.

According to the ABPI, the pharmaceutical industry employs over 75 000 people, a quarter of whom are graduates.

The companies within the ABPI research, develop, manufacture and supply nearly all of the medicines prescribed through the **National Health Service (NHS)**.

For further information, go to the section on manufacturing pharmaceuticals on the ABPI website, which can be accessed at http://www.abpischools.org.uk/resources/manufacturing/index.asp.

Alexander Fleming, the discoverer of penicillin

History of pharmaceuticals

In 1928 the microbiologist Alexander Fleming accidentally contaminated a petri dish containing bacteria with a mould known as penicillium.

While examining the plate, Fleming made an interesting discovery. He noticed that the bacteria on the agar medium were not growing in the vicinity of the mould.

From this observation he concluded that the mould must have been secreting something into the **agar medium** that was inhibiting the growth of the bacteria. What Fleming had discovered was the antibiotic now known as penicillin.

It was this chance discovery that formed the basis for the production of modern antibiotics and other drugs (substances that are used to relieve the symptoms of disease, pain and discomfort).

However, not all drugs come from microbes, and not all are used to treat infections. Other drugs are extracted from natural products such as plants and animals. Many modern drugs were developed with the aid of computers to alter the chemical nature of existing compounds.

The drug compound on its own is often too toxic or unstable for administration to a patient. It must first be subjected to a development and formulation programme that will ultimately convert it from a raw ingredient to a convenient and safe drug.

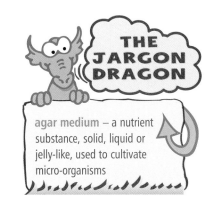

THE JARGON DRAGON

agar medium – a nutrient substance, solid, liquid or jelly-like, used to cultivate micro-organisms

Developing new drugs

Before a drug compound can be used as a medicine, it must first be subjected to a costly and rigorous programme of testing, development, formulation and clinical trials. This may take up to ten years and will involve modifications and tests on the drug formulation to ensure that it is safe to use, and to eliminate adverse side effects.

It is worth noting that some drugs initially developed for one purpose have ended up being used for an entirely different purpose. This may be because what were originally seen as side effects came to be regarded as more useful or beneficial than the original purpose. The manufacturers will alter the development and testing program to exploit these characteristics.

By law, before a drug can be marketed, it must be approved for use by the approved **government regulatory bodies** and **independent advisory committees**. This will involve an assessment of the benefits of the medicine versus the risks from any remaining adverse side effects.

Petri dishes with agar jelly

Formulation and design of pharmaceuticals

The type of formulation that is used to administer the drug to the patient is known as a dosage form or medicine. There are a number of different dosage forms available; some drugs are formulated into more than one type.

Some common examples include:

- **injection products**: sterile vials, ampoules, syringes
- **topical products**: creams, ointments, emulsions, lotions, drops, skin patches
- **inhalation products**: powder and liquid oral/nasal sprays
- **oral products:** tablets, capsules, syrups, elixir.

There are a number of factors that need to be taken into account when determining which type of formulation to use.

a) The chemical and physical properties of the drug.
- Is it soluble in water?
- Is it sensitive to light or heat?
- Is it unstable in acidic or alkaline conditions?
- Does it cause irritation to certain parts of the body?

b) How quickly is it needed in the body and what is the intended target?
- If a drug is required very quickly in the body, it may have to be injected directly into the bloodstream or muscle.
- In many cases it would be unnecessary for the drug to enter the bloodstream because its intended target is external. It may be necessary to release the drug more gradually to the affected area, in which case it could be applied topically to the affected area.

c) The cost of the formulation.

This would also be a factor in determining the type of dosage form. For example, it may be more economical for the manufacturer to produce the product as a syrup rather than a tablet.

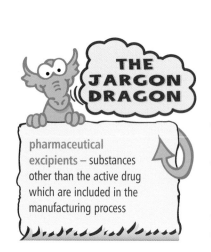

THE JARGON DRAGON

pharmaceutical excipients – substances other than the active drug which are included in the manufacturing process

In addition to the drug itself, all pharmaceutical preparations will contain a number of other non-active ingredients (**excipients**). They are designed to provide bulk and stability to the drug, and to assist in the manufacturing process.

Some excipients are added to help disperse the drug after administration to the patient, or to mask any unwanted aftertaste. This is particularly useful for child preparations.

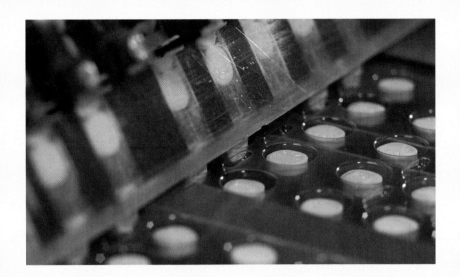

Tablets are manufactured by feeding a solid mass containing the drug and its pharmaceutical excipients into a shaped die (a series of wells). The mass is then compressed between two punches to form the tablet.

A typical tablet press will contain multiple dies and will enable the manufacturing process to run continuously.

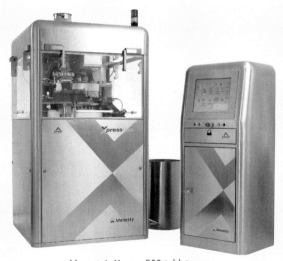

Manesty's Xpress 500 tablet press

The manufacture of tablets can be summarised into five steps, not all of which will be necessary for some types of tablet:

- **dispensing** – the drug and excipients are weighed or measured out
- **blending** – the excipients are mixed together to form a solid mass
- **granulation** – the solid mass is formed into uniform granules

- **compression** – the granules are fed into the tablet die and compressed
- **coating** – the tablet is spray coated, if required, in a separate process.

A typical tablet will contain the following excipients in addition to the drug itself:

- **lubricants** – designed to improve the powder flow properties and to prevent the finished tablet from sticking to the tablet press
- **diluent** – designed to provide bulk to the drug if the required dose is very small
- **granulating agents and binders** – used to aid the powder flow properties and to enable the ingredients to be compressed into a tablet
- **binders** – designed to prevent the tablet from breaking up when handled
- **disintegrants** – materials designed to swell when they come into contact with moisture, helping the tablet to break up when it is administered to the patient
- **coating agents** – provide a smooth surface to the tablet and help to mask any unpleasant flavours.

Pharmaceutical manufacture

There are numerous methods used to manufacture pharmaceutical products. They all depend on the type of product that is to be manufactured, and the regulatory guidelines that must be adhered to.

All pharmaceutical products fall into one of two broad categories:

- non-sterile products
- sterile products.

Non-sterile products

Non-sterile products such as creams, ointments, inhalers and tablets are manufactured in a controlled area, subject to strict personnel entry, exit and equipment cleaning programmes.

The products are manufactured to a high level of quality, and must meet pre-determined manufacture and testing specifications before they can be released to the market.

Sterile products

The guidelines governing the manufacture of sterile products are much more stringent than those for non-sterile products.

Sterile products are manufactured in an area called a clean room. The entry and exit of personnel, equipment, and materials must be very tightly controlled and documented.

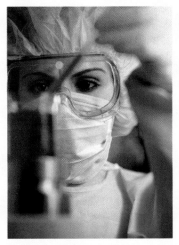 

Inside a clean room   A glove box facility

The quality of the incoming air supply and cleanliness of the area must also be closely monitored.

The immediate area around the filling and manufacture equipment is often enclosed and protected by additional high quality air filters.

Developments in sterile product manufacture have led to the introduction of **isolator facilities**, consisting of an enclosed cabinet or workstation with an attached equipment transfer port.

The workstations have integral glove ports that are designed to allow the operator to handle equipment and materials without coming into direct contact with them.

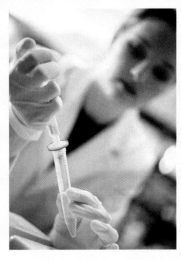

The cost of sterile manufacture is usually much greater than that of non-sterile manufacture.

For this reason, sterile manufacture is often reserved only for those products that are to be administered directly into the blood stream (for example, injections and infusion products).

Focus on the food industry

Food is one of the largest sectors of manufacturing. Employing billions of people worldwide, the industry fills our supermarkets and shops with the range of products we eat every day.

To investigate one small part of this industry, we will take a closer look at one of the products you might like to eat every week.

If you were to grow a load of potatoes in a field the size of a football pitch and then harvest them, these potatoes would last only one hour in the KP foods factory. In a plant that runs 24 hours a day, 7 days a week, you can imagine they get through a lot of spuds!

McCoy's crisps originate in fields like this one

McCoy's, a well known crisp brand, was launched in 1985. It is now the second best selling KP brand of food – this is what we are going to look at.

One thousand people work for KP foods in the Tees Valley, where there are teams of managers, food technologists, engineers and inspectors, working with teams of production operators to convert our humble potatoes into millions of bags of crisps.

From the gatehouse to the despatch of the crisps, dozens of teams communicate and co-operate closely with each other to produce the endless boxes of crisps and snacks that roll off the production line every day.

The importance of hygiene is evident everywhere – coveralls and hairnets are used to protect the food, and luminous vests ensure the safety of visitors and workers.

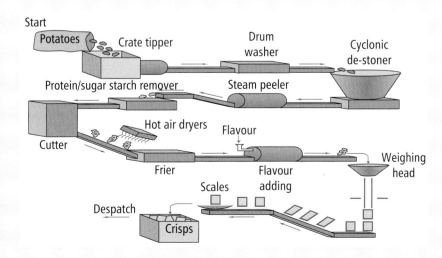

The process of making McCoy's crisps at KP Foods

case study

KP foods

Potatoes, specially grown for the production of crisps, arrive in sacks by the tonne. Lady Rosset and Saurna potatoes do not go soft after cooking like the regular potatoes that we use at home. They are sent through a cleaning and washing process which takes out stones, wood and dirt. For every 3000 kg of potatoes that enter the process, only 1000 kg are left to make the crisps.

Cyclonic de-stoner

Inspection of peeled potatoes

The cyclonic de-stoner creates a whirlwind inside a giant funnel to remove stones from the potatoes. The skins are stripped off instantly by jets of water – if any potatoes are too big, the pressure of the water blows them in half!

The process of crisp production is fully automated, but the inspection and quality control processes are all carried out by humans. The skill of the inspector's eye and taste buds can not be replaced by technology!

Green potatoes and burnt crisps are rooted out long before they reach the packing stage.

Inspection of cooked crisps

A team of maintenance engineers ensures that the plant operates efficiently, with little or no time wasted through breakdowns. Designers and production engineers are constantly looking at new and better ways to improve production.

Everyone in the company is part of the quality control team. They can see and taste the crisps at any stage, alerting quality control of any issues – not a bad job if you like crisps!

Portions of crisps fall into a **weighing head** which calculates the exact weight of the crisps. These fall into a tube of foil, sealed with a **pneumatic press**, to form the packet.

One of a series of weighing heads

Airtight packets are packed into boxes

The packets are tested for air leaks to verify the seal, and then boxed, ready for despatch.

Health and safety

Throughout this unit you will have seen that health and safety is extremely important. This section provides a little more general information about health and safety issues.

Working safely

You must always make sure that you are working safely and that you are not endangering yourself or others. This includes all the students, teachers and technicians in the workshop.

Behaviour

When you are working in a workshop, you need to be responsible and mature, because there are many dangers that you need to be aware of.

Be aware of:

- sharp tools and objects
- moving machinery such as lathes, milling machines and drills
- slippy floors from oil or coolant
- heated materials or ingredients
- irritant materials and ingredients that may cause allergies.

Always remember that fooling around in these situations can lead to serious injury.

Workshops and factories are often noisy and full of moving machinery. This can make students feel uncomfortable, tired or lose concentration. Be aware of this. Don't be afraid to tell someone if you are feeling tired or fed up.

Emergency stop buttons

These are found all around workshops. Pressing an emergency stop button will turn off the power to every machine in the workshop. They should only be switched off in an emergency.

FIND IT OUT

Look for all the emergency stop buttons in your workshop. How many are there?

There are various types of emergency stop button, all of which are large and red. Some have a key so that only a supervisor or teacher can switch the power back on.

If you see someone in danger, you should hit the emergency stop button, and tell your supervisor or teacher immediately.

Switching off an emergency stop button is a serious matter: never do it unless absolutely necessary.

THE JARGON DRAGON

risk assessment – a method of looking at a particular area or procedure to determine what risks are involved, so that a risk assessment form can be produced as guidance for safe practice

Supervision

Students should always be supervised in the workshop. If there is no teacher, **do not enter the workshop**.

Students should be careful with sharp edges on hand tools such as saws, needles or knives. You must inform a teacher when using machinery: some machines will need 100% supervision. The teacher will have made a **risk assessment** of all machines, so will know how much supervision is required. Always ask when you need to use a machine.

Personnel

There are many people who could be working in the workshop at the same time as you:

Job title	Job description
teacher	your main supervisor at school, who works with a college lecturer during college activities
college lecturer	your main supervisor at college
technician	supports teaching staff by cutting material, preparing equipment or carrying out many other tasks
stores person	holds all tools in the tool store, giving out materials, tools and equipment to support staff
first aider	treats injuries that occur
inspector	checks that teaching staff are teaching what they are supposed to, and that students are learning
other students	there may be other groups in the workshop, older or younger; respect all other students

Personal protective equipment

This term applies to any equipment that will protect you.

Anyone working in a workshop should have safety boots and overalls.

Goggles should always be worn when using machinery, or when there is a danger of sharp or hot objects hitting the face.

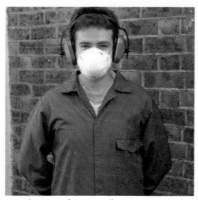

A student in safety overalls wearing ear defenders and a face mask

Helmet, ear defenders, goggles, gloves and face mask

Working with heat

When using heat in procedures such as the heat treatment of metals you will need special leather gloves to protect your hands and arms.

Make sure you use gloves to remove products from hot ovens.

If you are brazing or welding, you need special heat protection provided by a special mask and gloves.

Fire safety

Fire extinguishers are made for different purposes. It is important to recognise that each type should be used for a particular type of fire.

Here we see a range of fire extinguishers:

Protective equipment may prevent serious injury

Water
For wood, paper and solid material fires
DO NOT USE on liquid, electrical or metal fires

Powder
For liquid and electrical fires
DO NOT USE on metal fires

Foam
For use on liquid fires
DO NOT USE on electrical or material fires

Carbon Dioxide (CO$_2$)
For liquid and electrical fires
DO NOT USE on metal fires

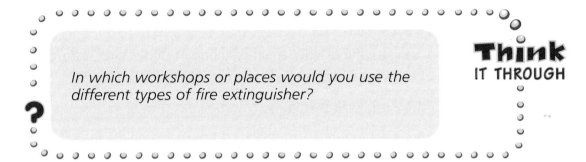

Think IT THROUGH

In which workshops or places would you use the different types of fire extinguisher?

Risk assessment

You should be able to look at a workshop and identify potential hazards, so that you can take precautions to prevent accidents happening. This is known as risk assessment. There are five steps to risk assessment:

Step 1: look for hazards

There are many places where accidents could occur. Look around the workshop: can you spot anything that might cause an accident?

Step 2: decide who might be harmed and how

Think of all the people who could be in a particular workshop or area. How could they be hurt? Often if people are unfamiliar with a place, they can be at risk.

Step 3: evaluate the risks and decide whether existing precautions are adequate, or whether more should be done

There may well be precautions in place, but ask yourself whether these are sufficient. Could the procedures be improved?

Step 4: record your findings

Write your findings down, so that you can refer to them at a later date.

Step 5: review your assessment and revise it if necessary

As time goes by, look at your risk assessment again. Have the risks changed? Do the procedures need to be changed?

Health and safety procedures

Students need to be able follow health and safety procedures and instructions. Sometime instructions can be complicated; if so, don't worry.

Remember to:

- listen
- ask the teacher again if you don't understand instructions
- stop and ask again if you cannot complete a task.

Think safety all the time!

You will be given instructions on how to complete tasks, the complexity of which will increase as you learn. You should learn easy procedures first, such as marking out and using hand tools. When you understand these procedures, you will be instructed how to use machines such as drilling machines. You will then move on to automatic machines such as milling machines and lathes. Safety procedures must be followed.

Fire drills

You will be given instructions about what to do in the event of a fire.

Fire drills are used to practise getting out of a building in the event of a fire. Fire instructions are usually found on the walls of workshops; ask a teacher if you cannot find them.

Remember:

- when the bell rings, leave the building with the teacher
- do not collect your belongings
- assemble at the point that you have been shown
- your teacher will call the register
- do not enter the building until told to do so by your teacher.
- if you spot a fire, sound the alarm.

FIND IT OUT

Follow the instructions which tell you how to get out of the building safely. How long does it take?

Housekeeping

Housekeeping refers to all those activities that keep your workplace clean and in good order. Good housekeeping leads to safer working areas and more accurate work.

Housekeeping can include:

- keeping your workshop area clean
- making sure that boots and overalls are not left on the floor
- making sure that coats and bags are kept in lockers
- cleaning up spillages
- clearing walkways
- storing tools and equipment properly in the store room
- cleaning and oiling machines after use
- keeping washing areas clean.

Maintenance of tools and equipment

Manufacturing tools are expensive; their quality will influence how good your work can be. All tools should be maintained, i.e. cleaned, lubricated and stored in their correct place. Machines for which maintenance is important include:

- printing presses
- machine tools
- sewing machines
- fabrication equipment.

These should be accompanied by manufacturer's documentation with details about lubrication, servicing and maintenance. These instructions must be followed.

Machinery

Machines use oils and coolants which can cause damage and create problems if left on a machine. You should expect a machine to be clean when you start work, and you should clean it down after use.

Applying quality and production control techniques

Consider the following question:

In manufacturing do you think that doing things right 99% of the time is good enough?

If you think the answer is 'no', you are quite correct – if, on the other hand, you think that 'yes, 99% is probably ok', take a look at the following list of examples of 99% quality standards.

- 13 major accidents at Heathrow Airport every 2 days
- 7 hours each month without electricity
- 100 minutes a week with television blackout
- 15 minutes a day without safe drinking water
- 5000 incorrect surgical procedures per week.

On the surface, a 99% level of performance seems excellent, but when you consider that a manufacturing company might produce 1 000 000 products a year, 99% quality would mean that 10 000 products would be defective. If each of these products cost £10 to make, £100 000 a year would be wasted due to poor quality.

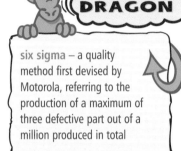

THE JARGON DRAGON

six sigma – a quality method first devised by Motorola, referring to the production of a maximum of three defective part out of a million produced in total

The process of maintaining standards to ensure that manufactured products are produced correctly is called **quality assurance**.

Modern manufacturing companies believe that it is unacceptable to produce any parts that are defective, and often aim for a target of producing only three in a million defective parts. Modern manufacturing companies use the term **six sigma** to describe quality at this level.

Quality is not a new idea; examples of high quality can be traced right back to the distant past:

Period in history	Example of high quality
Ancient Egypt	High consistency and geometric accuracy of pyramid building blocks
Ancient Greece	Precision and accuracy of pottery
Ancient Rome	Consistency of buildings and roads
Middle ages	Crafts and guilds became responsible for setting the standards for acceptable workmanship
Industrial revolution	High production levels of complex products, the quality of which was assessed by inspection/rejection
First World War	First book published on quality, invention of the control chart and first publication of the BSI
Second World War	Minimum quality levels established, and broad use of documentation such as work procedures
1950s and 1960s	Work by major quality pioneers such as Philip Crosby, William Deming and Joseph Juran increased quality within companies, underpinning much of the quality techniques used today

In modern manufacturing, quality is fundamental to all the activities undertaken within an organisation.

A popular definition of quality (first used by Joseph Juran) refers to a product that is 'fit for use', i.e. it does what it is intended to do.

According to this definition, a simple disposable razor can have a quality level as high as a Sony camcorder, as long as it performs as well as it has been designed to, and the customer is satisfied.

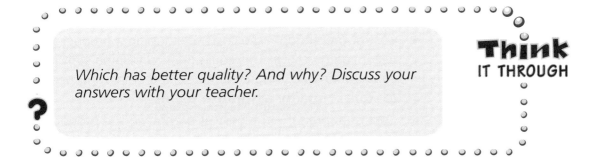

Think
IT THROUGH

Which has better quality? And why? Discuss your answers with your teacher.

?

Companies often employ personnel dedicated to ensuring that quality is constantly of a high standard. Thanks to the teaching of the early quality pioneers, it is now commonplace for all workers within a manufacturing company to be equally responsible.

The term total quality management (TQM) refers to the prioritising of quality, ensuring that all staff are responsible for maintaining and improving the quality of the finished product.

A simple Bic razor and state-of-the-art Sony camcorder are both associated with high quality

The cost of quality

Manufacturing companies generally invest lots of money on producing products to a required standard, for one simple reason: if a defective product reaches a customer, that customer will not be satisfied – if a customer is not satisfied, the company has failed with its product, which could lead to an eventual loss of reputation – loss of reputation will have a direct impact on sales, and therefore on profit.

Think
IT THROUGH

Consider which well known manufacturing companies are perceived to have excellent quality. Why do you think they have this reputation? Can you think of any companies with a reputation for poor quality?

Discuss your thoughts with a friend or teacher.

?

THE JARGON DRAGON

quality assurance teams – groups of company personnel with the specific task of improving quality within an organisation, often representing a cross-section of the workforce, and gathered from different departments

The impact of quality on a company can be measured in terms of the cost of quality. As much as 25% of a company's revenue can be used on quality costs. If a company earned £1 million a year, as much as £250 000 could be used on quality costs which can be grouped into six categories:

- Cost of prevention – the costs of stopping a product from becoming defective. This could refer to training staff in correct manufacturing techniques, and employing people to work in **quality assurance teams**.
- Cost of appraisal – the cost of producing the product to standard. This could refer to the staff employed to inspect and check products.
- Cost of internal failure – the cost of repairing or correcting defective products prior to delivery to a customer. It could include scrap, rework or design changes.
- Cost of external failure – the cost of repairing products after delivery to the customer. Warranty replacement parts and service, and replacement products are common examples.
- Cost of exceeding requirements – the cost of doing something that is unnecessary to a manufacturing company, for example, conducting a needless quality study or producing a report on something that is never manufactured.
- Cost of lost opportunities – the cost of lost sales from the loss of existing customers or the loss of potential customers.

Examples of this are cancellations resulting from delivery problems, or customers ordering a competitor's product because it has higher quality levels.

ACTIVITY

The manager of a small clothing company is worried about the amount of money being spent on quality improvement, so he decides to conduct a cost of quality study, and finds the following.

He employs seven full time staff, and has an annual turnover of £500 000.

The table below shows the cost of employing them.

Description	Number	Cost per person per year
Management	2	£40 000
Sales	1	£20 000
Maintenance	2	£21 000
Finance	1	£25 000
Quality assurance	1	£24 000

He discovers that:

- *one-fifth of one manager's time is spent on quality improvement*
- *half of quality assurance time is spent on inspection work*
- *half of maintenance time is spent dealing with breakdowns*
- *one-fifth of sales time is spent dealing with customer complaints*
- *one-fifth of finance time is spent checking invoices for errors*
- *£50 000 a year in sales is lost to competitors.*

Try to calculate the cost of quality, highlighting what category each of these findings would fall into, e.g. prevention, internal failure, etc.

Answers on page 321

Quality and process control techniques

To reduce the possibility of producing defective products and improve the overall quality, manufacturing companies use various techniques to monitor and control the product being processed.

This is often achieved by using a mixture of preventative measures, such as the careful control of equipment and machinery, and inspection methods, i.e. the measurement or checking of products to ensure they meet the required standard.

Inspection

The process of inspection generally involves examining a product closely to determine whether or not it has been produced to the required standard.

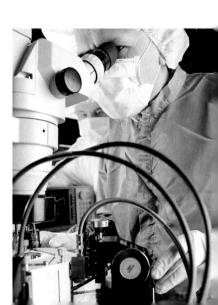

It can be carried out on every product (with low volume or high value products) or on a sample from a batch (for high volume or low value products).

Inspection is often carried out at each subsequent stage of the manufacturing process to determine if the product is satisfactory before being passed on to the next stage.

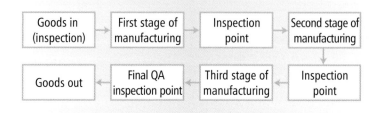

| Goods in (inspection) | → | First stage of manufacturing | → | Inspection point | → | Second stage of manufacturing |

| Goods out | ← | Final QA inspection point | ← | Third stage of manufacturing | ← | Inspection point |

Inspection can be classified into variable inspection and attributive inspection.

Variable inspection
Variable inspection is carried out on features which can be physically measured. For example, variable inspection could be used to measure:

- the length of a cut piece of fabric
- the weight of a packet of crisps
- the temperature of an oven
- electrical properties such as voltage and current
- the surface finish of a car door.

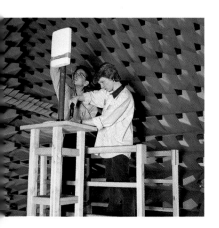

Nokia handsets being weighed – an example of variable inspection

To carry out this type of inspection, some form of measuring device or gauge is used. Common types of gauge include:

- measuring devices such as rules, vernier callipers or micrometers to measure length
- temperature gauges such as thermometers and thermocouples
- scales to measure weight
- multimeters to measure electrical properties.

Attributive inspection
Attributive inspection is used when a product is being appraised rather than measured.

For example, a box of chocolates would be checked to ensure that each individual piece is placed in the correct position. The chocolates are either present or not: hence the product will pass or fail.

Examples of attributive inspection are checking that:

- the labels have been placed on food containers
- all the keys have been placed on a computer keyboard
- all the bottles of water have been placed in a multi-pack
- all the pages are present within this book.

Attributive inspection at Speciality Welds

Attributive inspection is usually a little more difficult than variable inspection. Have a go at the following exercise.

Count the fs in the following passage:

The necessity of training hands for first class farms in the fatherly handling of farm livestock is foremost in the eyes of farm owners.

Since the forefathers of the farm owners trained the farm hands for first class farms in the fatherly handling of farm livestock, the farm owners feel they should carry on with the family tradition of training farm hands of first class farmers in the fatherly handling of farm live stock because they believe it is the fundamental basis of good farm management.

How many did you get?

Try the exercise again.

This time you will more than likely have a slightly different number. This activity highlights the main problem with attributive inspection – it relies heavily on the skill of the person inspecting the product to detect that all features and components are present and in the correct order.

Answers on page 321

Human error is commonly associated with attributive inspection and often occurs as a result of:

- not concentrating
- misunderstanding of standards
- poorly trained staff
- intentional neglect of standards
- tiredness or distraction
- products being incorrectly viewed and inspected
- work overload or uncomfortable working conditions
- lack of quality standards.

Companies often implement strategies to avoid many of the above, including the development of useful quality standards.

Quality standards come in many different forms, but all are designed to ensure that the product is made correctly.

Quality standards come in many different forms; the type of standard (or method used) varies from product to product.

Some examples of quality standards are:

- technical drawings
- work instructions
- checksheets
- quality tools.

Manufacturing companies with good quality procedures often use staff training sessions to make everyone in the company aware of their responsibilities in producing a product to the required standard.

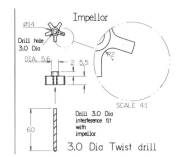

A technical drawing of an air drill

Controlling and recording quality

It is very common to use quality tools such as graphs and charts when working on quality projects. These tools can be very useful in summarising and analysing information gained from the manufacturing process.

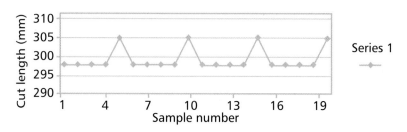

A4 paper cut length

For example, have a look at the simple line graph on the previous page – it represents A4 paper being cut to length. In this example, the length is measuring using automatic inspection. The results are recorded on a line graph.

Immediately you can see that numbers 1–4 are cut to the correct length (297 mm). However, sample number 5 jumps to 305 mm – this length then appears to be repeated every 5 samples.

Illustrated on this type of graph, the pattern is immediately obvious and inspectors would be instantly alerted to a problem within the process. However, this example has only 20 samples – just think how useful it would be if you were producing millions of the same product.

Further investigation would then need to then be carried out in order to determine the cause of the problem. In this case, factors could be the equipment, the operator, the material or a combination of these three.

Common quality tools
Boardstorming or mind mapping
Boardstorming, sometimes called mind mapping, is a technique used to improve the quality of a product by allowing personnel from a cross-section of the organisation to express their views in a relaxed, unthreatening and informal environment.

The session should last only about ten minutes, and all suggestions (no matter how abstract) are welcomed. The suggestions are often recorded on a flip chart, wipeboard or notepad.

The comments can then be examined in more detail and investigated further, hopefully leading to a quality improvement.

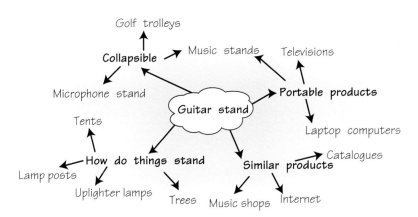

A designer's mind map

Cause–effect diagrams

Cause–effect diagrams are used to show visually what could cause a product to become defective (faulty).

The factors that could lead a product to go wrong are arranged in groups to show their relationship to each other and the final problem.

The diagram is often called a fishbone diagram because it looks like a fishbone.

Have a look at the example below, showing a non-manufacturing problem of a car losing control.

A quality team has found that there are four groups of factors causing the car to lose control.

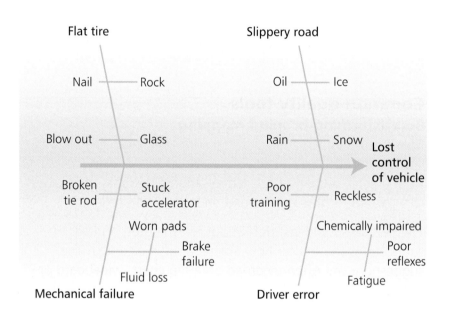

A cause–effect diagram – reprinted with permission from Juran Institute, Inc.

Flow diagrams

Quality teams often use flow diagrams to help to understand a manufacturing process. Often, manufacturing processes are very complex: this type of diagram is used to simplify the process by showing all the steps required to produce the final product.

By examining this type of diagram, quality teams can often make changes to the sequence of operation, and make quality improvement suggestions.

Graphs and charts

Various graphs and charts are used in quality assurance, depending on the type of quality checks being undertaken. Some

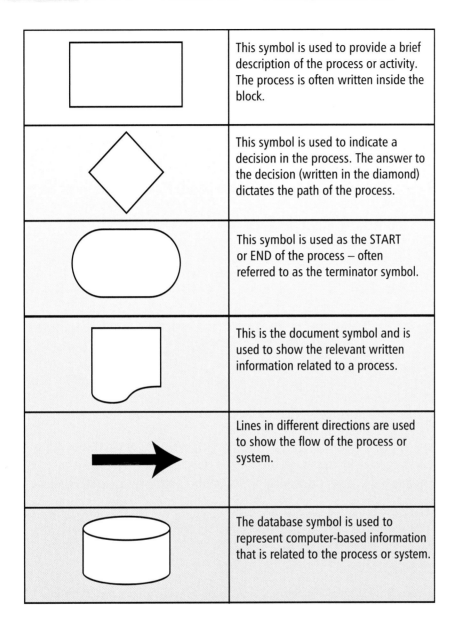

	This symbol is used to provide a brief description of the process or activity. The process is often written inside the block.
	This symbol is used to indicate a decision in the process. The answer to the decision (written in the diamond) dictates the path of the process.
	This symbol is used as the START or END of the process – often referred to as the terminator symbol.
	This is the document symbol and is used to show the relevant written information related to a process.
	Lines in different directions are used to show the flow of the process or system.
	The database symbol is used to represent computer-based information that is related to the process or system.

Symbols used in flow diagrams (all of these symbols and more can be found in Microsoft Word within Autoshapes – Flowchart

common types are bar diagrams, pie charts, line graphs, scatter diagrams and histograms.

Bar diagrams

Bar diagrams are used to show the relationship between two different variables. Quality teams often use this type of chart to compare data across one variable, e.g. day to day, machine to machine, operator to operator.

For example, the diagram on the next page shows the average output of training shoes being made on each day of the week.

Variable 1 is the day of the week (x-axis); variable 2 is the output of training shoes (y-axis).

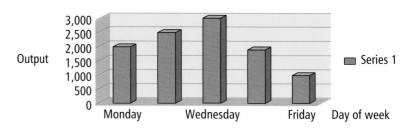

Training shoe output plotted against day of the week

From this example you can see that not as many training shoes have been made on Friday. This is because it is a half day in the company.

Pie charts

Pie charts are used to show the relative proportions of parts making up a whole group.

Each segment refers to the size of a factor, i.e. the larger the segment, the larger the factor's contribution to the whole group.

For example, the pie chart here shows the different types of soft drink made in one week. As you can see, more cola was made than any other soft drink in this week.

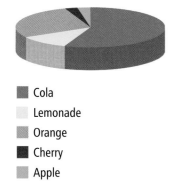

- Cola
- Lemonade
- Orange
- Cherry
- Apple

Line graphs

As the name suggests, line graphs are used to illustrate a topic of interest (process outcome, cost, errors, etc.) by plotting measured values and connecting them together using a series of short lines.

They are often used by quality teams to show if a measured value is rising, falling or remaining the same, often over a long period of time.

For example, the line chart below illustrates the non-conforming number of chocolate covered biscuits (those not produced to standard) per week over a 30-week cycle.

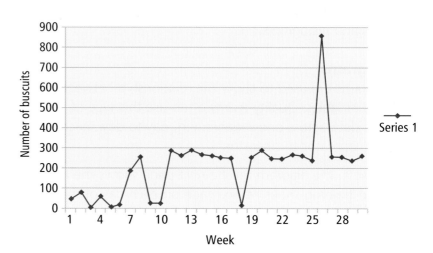

Biscuits not produced to standard

A more advanced quality tool which utilises a line graph to illustrate its outcomes is statistical process control (SPC).

SPC is a technique used to determine if a process is in control or not, i.e. if it is producing components to a satisfactory level of quality.

The technique works by calculating a process average and using this value to determine the upper and lower limits that are seen to be acceptable.

The average, acceptable limits and individually measured values are placed on a chart like the following one.

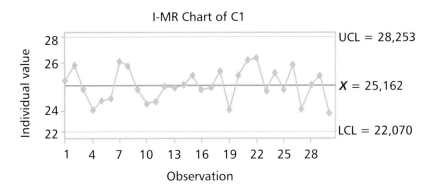

Here, the upper and lower control limits are 28.253 and 22.070 respectively

This technique is often used by quality teams and is very common in the manufacturing of automotive and electronic components.

Scatter diagrams

Scatter diagrams are used to illustrate the relationship between two measured variables in a process.

The scatter diagram below shows the relationship between the average number of operator errors on a production line and the experience of the operator in terms of months of service.

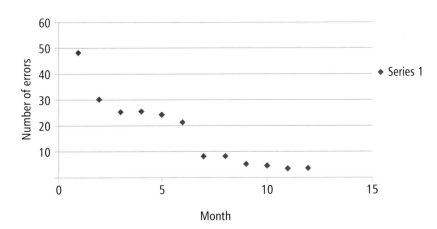

The diagram indicates that as operators spend more time in the company, they make fewer errors.

Histograms

Histograms are used to show the variation and frequency within a set of values, i.e. to show how the values in a set differ, and how often this occurs.

They were developed in 1833 by the French statistician A. M. Guerry, as a kind of bar graph used to record and analyse crime data.

Today the histogram remains a useful tool, because it allows the viewer to see the full range of data arranged in a pictorial way.

In a histogram, the spread of data is arranged into convenient groups, often using a tally chart.

The groups (or categories) are placed on the horizontal axis; the frequency of their occurrence is placed on the vertical axis.

The tally chart on the left shows the age of employees in a food processing factory.

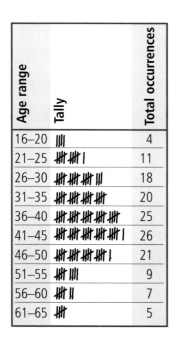

Age range	Tally	Total occurrences
16–20	IIII	4
21–25	HHT HHT I	11
26–30	HHT HHT HHT III	18
31–35	HHT HHT HHT HHT	20
36–40	HHT HHT HHT HHT HHT	25
41–45	HHT HHT HHT HHT HHT I	26
46–50	HHT HHT HHT HHT I	21
51–55	HHT IIII	9
56–60	HHT II	7
61–65	HHT	5

The data are then transferred to the histogram.

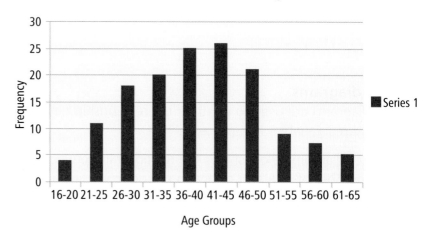

You can see that more people within the company fall into the age brackets of 36–40 and 41–45 than any other.

Statistics used in quality assurance

Statistics are quite often used in quality assurance work to help understand and interpret information gathered from the manufacturing process. This is an area of expertise which can become very complex and require a lot of training to fully understand in detail.

Put simply, statistics is the gathering, organising, studying and presentation of information.

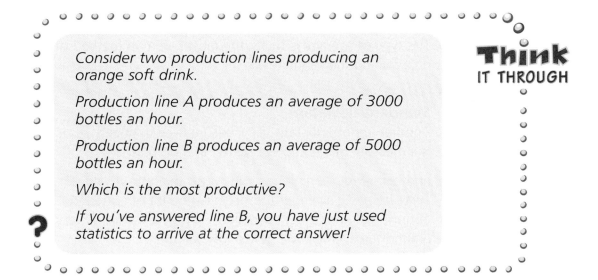

Think
IT THROUGH

Consider two production lines producing an orange soft drink.

Production line A produces an average of 3000 bottles an hour.

Production line B produces an average of 5000 bottles an hour.

Which is the most productive?

If you've answered line B, you have just used statistics to arrive at the correct answer!

Average values

An average is a useful and common method of measuring the central tendency (central value) of a variable, and can take three forms, the mode, the median and the mean:

The **mode** is the most common output from a process, for example:

   2   2   3   3   3   4   4   4   4   5   (all mm)

In this case the mode would be 4 mm, which is the most common value, appearing on four occasions.

The **median** is the middle value when all outputs are arranged in numerical order, for example:

   2   2   3   3   (3   4)   4   4   4   5   (all mm)

In this example, the middle values are 3 mm and 4 mm, so the median would be 3.5 mm, halfway between 3 mm (the 5th value) and 4 mm (the 6th value).

The **mean** is a mathematical value represented by the following simple equation:

$$\text{Mean} = \frac{\text{all the individual values added together}}{\text{number of outputs}}$$

For example,

   2   2   3   3   3   4   4   4   4   5   (all mm)

$$\text{Mean} = \frac{2 + 2 + 3 + 3 + 3 + 4 + 4 + 4 + 4 + 5}{10}$$

$$= \frac{34}{10} = 3.4 \text{ mm.}$$

This type of average is by far the most common method of determining the central value.

Standard deviation

Another important statistical measure used in quality assurance is a measure of variation or scatter in a process.

In other words, variation is how much the output values move away from the average. A process with a lot of scattered outputs will have a high variation – a process which is very tight around the average will have a low variation.

The most common measure of variation is the standard deviation.

The standard deviation is obtained by using a formula, and works by examining the variation of each individual value, compared with the mean.

In other words it compares each value in the sample with the average, to determine how far from the average each value actually is – these values are then used to obtain a figure that describes the variation or spread of numbers.

For example, suppose an operator is set a task of sharpening five pencils to a length of 8 mm.

The operator finds this task more difficult than expected, and produces five pencils with sharpened lengths of 6.5 mm, 8.2 mm, 8.5 mm, 7.5 mm, and 7 mm.

The first stage of the analysis requires the mean length. This can be obtained by adding all the individual values together and dividing by the number of outputs.

$$\text{So, the mean} = \frac{6.5 + 8.2 + 8.5 + 7.5 + 7}{5} = 7.54 \text{ mm.}$$

The standard deviation can then be calculated, using the following formula:

$$\text{Standard deviation} = \sqrt{\left[\frac{(\text{each value} - \text{mean average})^2}{\text{number of values} - 1}\right]}$$

$$= \sqrt{\left[\frac{[(6.5 - 7.54)^2 + (8.2 - 7.54)^2 + (8.5 - 7.54)^2 + (7.5 - 7.54)^2 + (7 - 7.54)^2]}{5 - 1}\right]}$$

$$= \sqrt{\left[\frac{[1.08 + 0.44 + 0.92 + 0.0016 + 0.29]}{4}\right]}$$

$$= \sqrt{0.68} = 0.83$$

You will probably agree that this calculation involves a lot of work to achieve just one number, which is why ICT is often used.

It is immediately obvious in this example that the operator hasn't done very well, but remember that thousands of products are often manufactured each hour, day or week (depending on the process), which is why a sample of values is generally used for this type of exercise.

A good manufacturing process will have an average that is very close to the target value (297.00 mm in our earlier A4 example) and a very small standard deviation (ideally a value approaching 0).

Using a large piece of paper (or a wipeboard if you are at school or college), mark a target 70 inches from the floor. (For the purpose of this exercise it's easier to work in imperial (inches) rather than metric units (cm or mm).

Now mark horizontal lines above and below the target every 2 inches.

Make a simple paper aeroplane and throw it 30 times at the target.

The aim of the activity is to hit the target within a range of 4 inches.

Copy down your results on the following tally chart.

Range	Tally
e.g. 20–32	|||| (4)
63–65	
65–67	
67–69	
69–71	
71–73	
73–75	
75–77	

Calculate your average (mean), and use the tally chart to construct a histogram. Draw in vertical lines to represent the target value (70 inches), the limits (68 inches and 72 inches), and the average.

Compare your results with the classmates. Consider the following points:

- Are all of your attempts between the limits?
- Are your attempts spread out?
- Is your mean near to the target of 70 inches?
- Could the aeroplane be improved?

ICT used for Quality Assurance and links to Unit 3: Application of Technology

You will probably have noticed that the graphs used in this section have not been drawn by hand, but using software such as Microsoft Excel.

Computers are used frequently in quality assurance work to input, measure, analyze and interpret information, by making calculations and producing graphs and charts.

Excel is described in more detail within Unit 3: Application of Technology, but another useful software package for quality assurance work is Minitab.

Visit the website at http://www.minitab.com. A demo version is often available, which can be used to calculate statistics such as the mean and standard deviation, in addition to producing some excellent graphs and charts.

Manufactured products quiz

1 Which software is usually used for production planning?

- CAD
- CAM
- Microsoft Excel
- Microsoft Outlook

2 What is a 'processing time'?

3 Which of the following is not a real type of resource used in manufacturing?

- human resource
- tooling resource
- health and safety resource
- intermediate resource

4 What is ISO 9000?

- a quality standard
- a type of material
- a piece of equipment
- a test taken by health and safety personnel

5 Finish the sentence 'The stages of manufacturing are: material preparation, processing, assembly, finishing and   .'

6 Which of the following might a personnel manager produce?

- production specification
- project plan
- organisation chart
- safety poster

7 What is generally the first stage of disciplining an individual who has misbehaved at work?

- verbal warning
- dismissal
- written warning
- final written warning

8 What is a common method of processing metals?

- injection moulding
- investment casting
- slip casting
- blow moulding

9 What does PPE stand for in health and safety information?

10 Is a 99% quality standard good enough in manufacturing?

Answers on page 321

What's in this unit?

To complete this unit you will need to understand the impact of new technology on engineering and manufactured products. You will learn that, whilst products can be categorised into different sectors of engineering and manufacture, they all utilise new technology.

You will investigate the impact of information and communications technology on businesses and you will investigate the impact of new components and a range of modern materials, including smart materials, in the engineering industry. You will learn about the changing systems of control technology and how modern engineering has developed because of this technology.

Application of Technology

In this unit you will learn about:

The manufacturing and engineering
sectors   242

The use of information and
communications technology   248

New materials and components   273

Systems and control technology   287

The application of technology   301

Exam hints   318

Revision questions   319

The manufacturing and engineering sectors

There is such an extensive range of products available that they are usually identified by grouping them into the following categories or **sectors**.

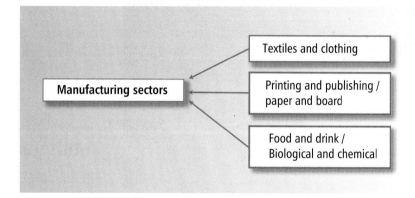

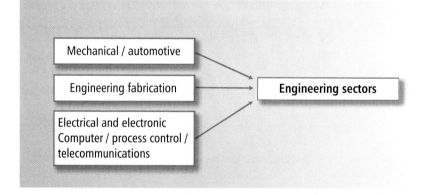

Manufacturing sectors

The first of the manufacturing sectors is concerned with the production of fabrics, textiles and clothing. The **textiles and clothing sector** contains a huge number of different products, including all fashion such as clothing and footwear, as well as curtains, upholstery, carpets and many others.

Every time you read a book, a newspaper or a magazine, or write in a notebook or diary, you are using products from the **printing and publishing sector** of manufacturing. The many different types of paper and board used for packaging, toilet rolls and tissues are all examples of paper and board production.

A few examples of the vast numbers of magazines that are included within the printing and publishing sector of manufacturing

The textiles and clothing sector of manufacturing relies heavily on the fashion industry for the promotion of their products

The final sector is arguably the easiest of the six to classify – **food and drink, chemical and biological**. Popular products such as cola and lemonade, crisps, chocolate, in addition to other fresh, frozen and tinned food, all fall into this category. Examples of chemical and biological products would include toiletries such as shower gel and deodorant, household cleaning products, and pharmaceutical products such as headache tablets and cough medicine.

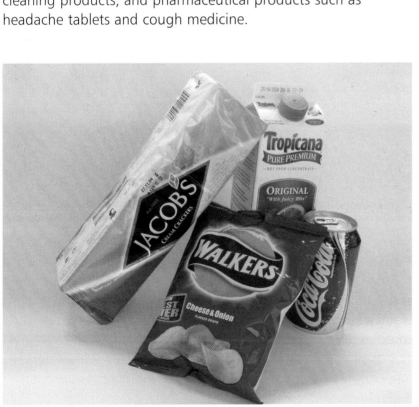

Various well known household products that fit into the sector of food and drink, chemical and biological

A mountain bike or BMX is a fabricated product. These are generally made of metal tubing formed and cut into shape before being joined together using a welding process

A less familiar fabricated product is a gas rig. These huge fabrications require vast amounts of labour, materials and equipment. They cost many millions of pounds to fabricate

The sector of electronic and electrical, computing and telecommunications is one of the fastest developing in technology. Just think of a computer five years ago compared with the latest models – the computer above is small enough to hold in the palm of your hand!

Engineering sectors

The **mechanical/automotive sector** includes products that are powered mechanically or automatically. Examples of products that fit into this sector include cars, vans, drills, presses, motorbikes, forklift trucks, power tools and many industrial machines.

The **fabrication sector** is perhaps the most difficult to classify. Products within this sector are generally defined as those that are made directly from raw materials such as sheet, plate, strip and bar. Generally, fabrication is associated with the joining and assembly of metal products, but other materials such as plastics and wood are also widely used.

Products in this sector include furniture, car parts, bridges, oil modules (rigs), hand tools, railings and gates, shopping trolleys, goalposts and mountain bikes.

Products that contain electrical or electronic components such as TVs, DVDs, microwaves or other kitchen appliances, lighting and CD players fit into the third sector – **electronic and electrical, computer and telecommunications**. Games consoles, laptop, personal and palmtop computers are all examples of the computer element of the sector, while Internet modems, digital and mobile phones are examples of products in the telecommunications sector.

Each of the segments in the diagram below represents a sector of engineering/manufacturing. Look at the pictures of the products and decide which sector they each belong to.

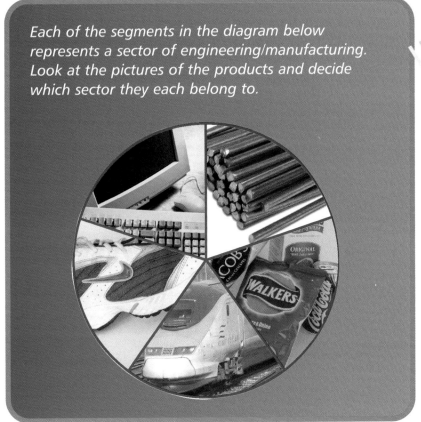

Turnover of the major sectors of manufacturing and engineering

The table below shows a breakdown of the major industries associated with manufacturing and engineering, and their annual **turnover**.

THE JARGON DRAGON

turnover – the total sales achieved by a company or organisation

Industry sector	Rank	Turnover (£ millions)
Food products, beverages and tobacco	1	75,019
Electrical equipment	2	65,007
Transport equipment	3	60,874
Chemical products	4	47,530
Printing and publishing, paper and paper products	5	45,981
Metals and fabricated products	6	41,081
Manufacture of machinery and equipment	7	33,522
Petroleum products and nuclear fuel	8	26,383
Polymer production	9	19,673
Textile production	10	13,502

The 'rank' column shows the position of each sector when they are ordered according to gross turnover. The sector with the highest grossing turnover (in millions of pounds) earned in 2001 is ranked number 1.

The stages of manufacturing and engineering a product

Most products that are engineered or manufactured follow a similar pattern from design, through production until they finally end up in the hands of the customer.

The stages of manufacturing and engineering are shown below.

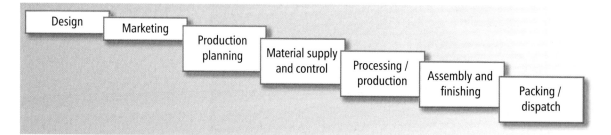

The first part of any production activity is the design stage. It doesn't matter if it's a pair of trainers, an oil rig or a DVD player, all need to be accurately designed and developed.

In the past, designing would be carried out on drawing boards by highly skilled designers and drawing office personnel. The use of computer programs is now very widespread, and the vast majority of final design work is carried out using specialist software.

This specialist software is often termed **computer-aided design** or CAD for short – we will discuss this later in the book.

Products are generally designed for two main reasons:

- to provide a functional solution to a problem (i.e. design a brand new item for a specific reason)
- to improve the performance or aesthetics of an existing product.

The process of doing research to find gaps in the consumer market is part of the **marketing** process. Information is often obtained through customer **questionnaires** and **feedback**. Have you ever bought a product and sent back a question card to the manufacturer with your thoughts on how good you think the product is? If the answer is yes then you have contributed to a marketing campaign.

Production planning and **material supply and control** are often closely linked. They are part of the process of organising a company to produce the right amount of product, in the right order, using the right materials and equipment. This is often done by specialist production planning personnel working closely with stock controllers and purchasing departments. Together they ensure that the right amount of product is manufactured at the right time.

Processing and **production**, **assembly** and **finishing** are also closely linked. These are the actual manufacturing and/or engineering involved in producing a product. This stage of production is often highly automated, accurate and economical. It is possibly the most interesting stage in the production process – quite simply, it's where things get made!

Processing and production involves the actual making of the various parts and components, while assembly is the process of fitting these individual parts together. Finishing is the process of cleaning up or applying final touches to a product – painting or varnishing, for example.

The final stages are **packing** and **despatch**. In these stages the products are securely wrapped up and then sent to the distributors and retailers who eventually sell the products to us.

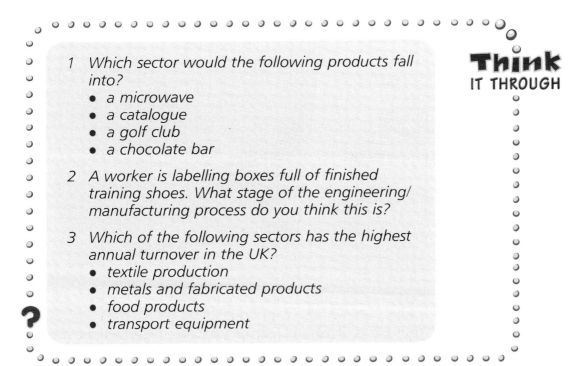

Think IT THROUGH

1 Which sector would the following products fall into?
   • a microwave
   • a catalogue
   • a golf club
   • a chocolate bar

2 A worker is labelling boxes full of finished training shoes. What stage of the engineering/manufacturing process do you think this is?

3 Which of the following sectors has the highest annual turnover in the UK?
   • textile production
   • metals and fabricated products
   • food products
   • transport equipment

The use of information and communications technology

Information and communications technology, or **ICT**, is as widespread in manufacturing and engineering as it is in the home.

Companies use ICT every day in their production processes, and without it customers like us would not have the range and quality of technically advanced products available today.

There is a good chance that you are familiar with the popular ICT packages such as wordprocessors, spreadsheets, databases and Internet sites, as these are often very well used in school, college or at home. We will come to these later, but first let's start with the ICT used to design a product.

CAD is used all over the world to design products, from housing estates to mobile phones. It can be used to make layout plans, component drawings and 3D models.

THE JARGON DRAGON

CAD – computer-aided design. It involves the use of computers to carry out design work that used to be carried out manually

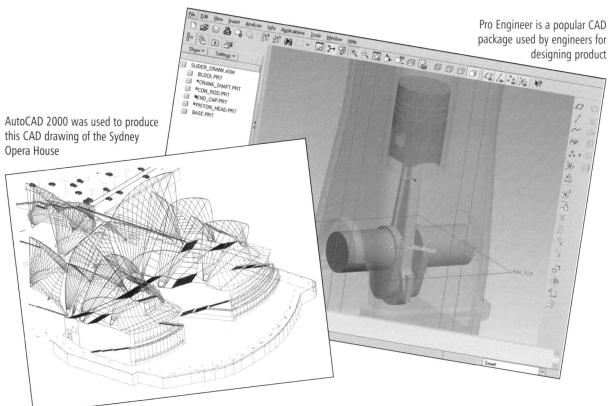

Pro Engineer is a popular CAD package used by engineers for designing product

AutoCAD 2000 was used to produce this CAD drawing of the Sydney Opera House

Even films such as *Shrek* and *Lord of the Rings* use an advanced type of CAD to construct their visual effects.

What is CAD?

You are probably already familiar with computer packages to help with design. Desktop publishing software, and graphics packages such as CorelDraw and Adobe Photoshop, are among the commercially available software used for computer design.

In industry, CAD generally refers to software packages that can produce high quality drawings and computer-generated models to exact specifications. Such packages enable the operator to draw objects very quickly, effectively and accurately. They can open, display and print drawings produced by other people that may have been sent on disk or by e-mail.

A popular package used for image manipulation is Adobe Photoshop

The main advantages of using CAD

Using CAD saves vast amounts of time and money. This means CAD has several key benefits:

- it produces drawings to a high standard and accuracy that is repeatable time and time again
- it can produce drawings more quickly than manual methods – this can lead to financial savings due to reduced labour costs
- it can carry out a range of drawing functions including 2D and 3D
- it is user-friendly and requires less manual skill to produce high quality drawings
- it is easy to open and modify existing drawings, which can then be printed, saved to hard drive, floppy disk or CD, or even e-mailed around the world

- standard parts such as screws, nuts and bolts can be pre-drawn and imported into drawings. This saves time, as the designer does not need to draw them from scratch each time he or she produces a new drawing.

Are there any disadvantages?

Yes, despite its many advantages CAD does have several disadvantages and limitations. They are:

- people may require special training to be able to use CAD – this can be expensive
- the software can be expensive to buy
- fewer people are needed to carry out drawing work because it is so much quicker than manual methods – this means fewer draughtsmen are required
- some CAD packages are not compatible with others, which may hinder the development of some products if different companies use different systems. A package called AutoCAD tends to be standard in many companies.

What is required to run a CAD system?

Standard CAD packages can run on normal domestic computers, like the one you may have at home. More advanced packages might require more memory and higher processor speeds in order to run effectively.

The diagram below summarises the important pieces of **hardware** and **software** required to run a CAD system:

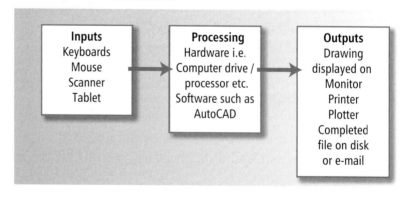

Inputs	Processing	Outputs
Keyboards Mouse Scanner Tablet	Hardware i.e. Computer drive / processor etc. Software such as AutoCAD	Drawing displayed on Monitor Printer Plotter Completed file on disk or e-mail

How does CAD work?

Drawing using CAD is very similar to drawing by hand. The screen is your piece of paper and the functions (line, circle, polygon, etc.) are your drawing tools.

Most technical CAD packages use a system of **co-ordinates** and **dimensions** to determine the exact position and size of features.

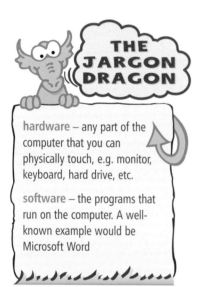

THE JARGON DRAGON

hardware – any part of the computer that you can physically touch, e.g. monitor, keyboard, hard drive, etc.

software – the programs that run on the computer. A well-known example would be Microsoft Word

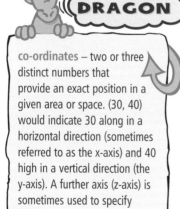

THE JARGON DRAGON

co-ordinates – two or three distinct numbers that provide an exact position in a given area or space. (30, 40) would indicate 30 along in a horizontal direction (sometimes referred to as the x-axis) and 40 high in a vertical direction (the y-axis). A further axis (z-axis) is sometimes used to specify depth.

For an example of a CAD package, take a look at the screenshot of the house plan below:

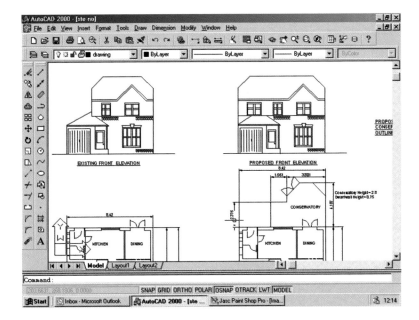

The **drawing area** is where the actual work is displayed, in two or three dimensions. This part of the screen represents the paper and it shows you what would be printed out. The drawing area can be changed to suit any paper size and the operator can zoom in very accurately without distorting the image. Likewise, any part of the drawing can be selected and printed – this is very useful when working with large products, for example vehicles such as cars.

The **drawing tools** are the basic commands used to create CAD drawings. The **tool bar** is shown to the right in more detail with descriptions of the most common commands.

The **command bar** is used to input commands using the keyboard. For example, to draw a line you would need to type in the command bar the command (in this case 'line' or 'L'), and the starting and ending co-ordinates.

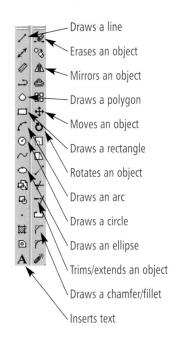

Draws a line

Erases an object

Mirrors an object

Draws a polygon

Moves an object

Draws a rectangle

Rotates an object

Draws an arc

Draws a circle

Draws an ellipse

Trims/extends an object

Draws a chamfer/fillet

Inserts text

e.g. Line from 30,40 (to) 100,50

This would result in the screen shown at the top of the next page – note the text within the highlighted command bar:

Many of the other functions or commands work in much the same way.

By using a variety of shapes and features with very accurate co-ordinates it is possible to design the vast amount of manufacturing and engineering products available today.

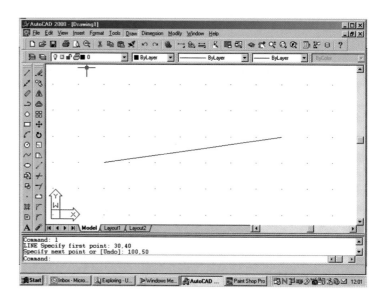

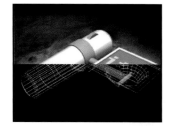

The finished product design can be displayed in two or three dimensions, as wire-frame or rendered images – modern packages can also animate objects to show multiple sides and faces in a range of angles and views.

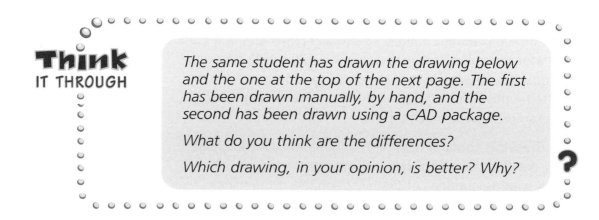

Think
IT THROUGH

The same student has drawn the drawing below and the one at the top of the next page. The first has been drawn manually, by hand, and the second has been drawn using a CAD package.

What do you think are the differences?

Which drawing, in your opinion, is better? Why?

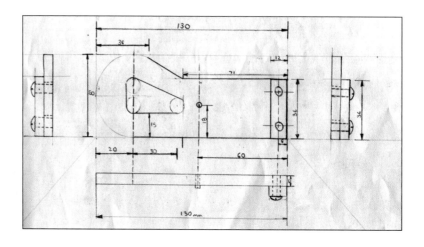

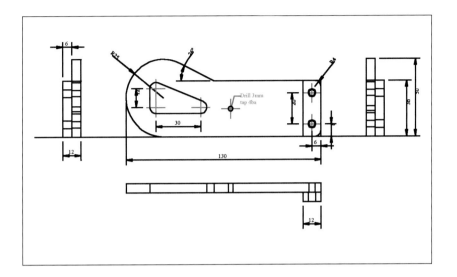

Introduction to CAM

The twentieth century saw massive technical improvements leading to the invention of many fundamental manufacturing techniques. Robotics, automation and computer technology were all developed in the last century and now contribute significantly to the range of products we have available today.

The list below shows how some of the key manufacturing and engineering techniques and processes were developed within the twentieth century.

- **1920:** first use of the word 'robot'
- **1920–1940:** mass production boom, first use of transfer machines
- **1940:** first electronic computer
- **1943:** first digital computer
- **1945:** first use of the word 'automation'
- **1952:** first prototype of a CNC machine
- **1954:** development of NC programming code
- **1957:** first commercially available NC machine tools
- **1960:** first use of industrial robots and CAD systems
- **1970:** first integrated manufacturing system
- **1970:** further development of CNC systems
- **1980s to present:** development of CAM techniques.

Adapted from: Serope Kalpakjian,'Manufacturing Processes for Engineering Materials'

Some of the words above may not be clear to you – don't worry, they will be explained within the next few pages.

Computer-aided manufacturing

Computer-aided manufacturing (CAM) allows computers to be used to design, develop and manufacture products with very little effort compared to more conventional techniques.

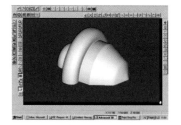

This means a product can be designed on a computer using CAD and then transferred to a CAM package. It is also possible to draw a component from scratch with many CAM packages.

The computer-generated design can then be given further information that is required to process the product. The additional information could be:

- materials to be used
- equipment and machinery required
- sequence (or order) of operations to carry out manufacturing.

Once the software package has all the required information it can then produce a program that the manufacturing process can understand.

This program is termed **numerical control (NC)**, and as computers carry out the transfer link, the process is termed **computer numerical control (CNC)**.

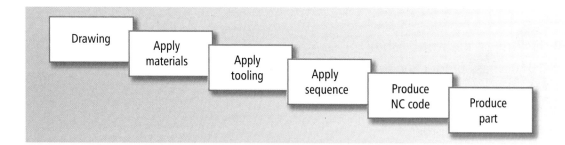

The manufacturing system is then used to produce the actual product or part of the product. In some cases it is used to make moulds or tools used in another process to manufacture the finished product.

Computer numerical control

Until the mid-1950s machinery used to cut and form was generally operated by two main methods.

- Manual operation (which is still widely used today) is carried out by very highly skilled workers who use various wheels, levers and controls to adjust the machinery to manufacture the required component. Measuring devices such as micrometers (see Unit 2) are used to control the accuracy and subsequent quality of the product. Altering and reworking are still very common to the process.

- For operations used to make a high volume of products, automatic operations tended to be more economical. These processes were faster and more reliable than manual methods but they did prove expensive to set up. This was because of the control systems, which used mechanical gears, cams and pulleys.

A traditional milling machine (left) and a CNC milling machine (right)

Numerical control changed all this. Numerical control used a program which described in exact detail the movement of the machine required to produce a part. The tooling would also be included, and the program could be used to produce identical parts over and over again.

In the early days the machinery didn't possess the memory capabilities that computers have today, and the program had to

A plasma-cutting process utilising a CNC system

be fed into the processor via punched paper – later plastic cassette tape was used.

Computer numerical control was a development that further improved the processing of products. By programming directly into the machine's memory using consoles, there was no longer any need to provide a tape copy of the program.

Operators could be given a drawing of the component and then, using a specific code, could program the machine to work automatically. The machine could then be set to work, allowing the operator to move (if required) to another workpiece or job.

This was a tremendous leap forward, and with the innovation of CAM, manufacturing high quality products to exact specifications was made even easier.

Manufacturing systems that are commonly linked to CNC include:

- drilling and milling machines
- cutting and welding operations
- bending and forming machines.

Typical products that use CAM techniques in their production include:

- scooters
- mobile phones
- games consoles
- trainers
- food packaging
- televisions
- CD players
- football boots
- water bottles
- office furniture
- mountain bikes
- shower gel containers.

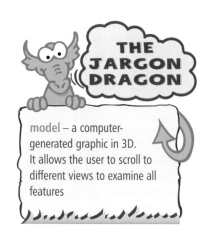

THE JARGON DRAGON

model – a computer-generated graphic in 3D. It allows the user to scroll to different views to examine all features

How does CAM work?

The exact operation of computer-aided manufacturing varies from system to system, but it generally follows the stages:

- generate a computer drawing or 3D **model**
- decide what processes are to be used
- tell the computer how to manufacture it, i.e. what tools and sequences are to be used
- if necessary, use the software to 'prove' the sequence before actually making the product
- generate the numerical code (NC) program
- send it to the machine
- set the machine going and make the product.

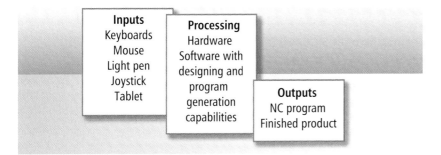

CAM has various advantages over more traditional manufacturing and engineering techniques. For example:

- it is easier to make technically complicated components
- it produces high quality products that are very accurate, time and time again
- it is more efficient than traditional methods, i.e. it is quicker and can produce high volumes of product
- programming can be carried out off-line in specific design offices and programs downloaded to machines in a different area
- operators do not need to be as highly skilled as those operating traditional processes.

The advantages of CAM to companies usually outweigh the disadvantages; however you need to note the following:

- it can initially be very expensive to set up CAM systems
- it can reduce the number of staff required in a company, leading to fewer employment opportunities
- as machine operation is largely controlled by technology, it can lead to a reduced level of skill among operators
- some systems can have compatibility problems with others, making file transfer between them difficult.

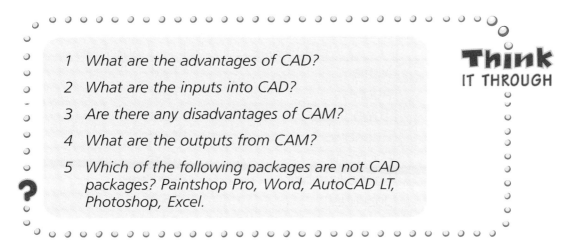

1 What are the advantages of CAD?

2 What are the inputs into CAD?

3 Are there any disadvantages of CAM?

4 What are the outputs from CAM?

5 Which of the following packages are not CAD packages? Paintshop Pro, Word, AutoCAD LT, Photoshop, Excel.

Think
IT THROUGH

Databases

A database, in simple terms, is an organised collection of information (or **data**, as the information is often termed).

You may or may not be aware that your own details are kept on many databases right now:

- at school or college
- at the doctor's, dentist or hospital
- at the local video store
- at youth centres and sports clubs.

This data can often include personal information such as your name, address, telephone number, age or height.

In industry, companies use databases for several reasons:

- **information on employees:** including personal details, salaries and job descriptions
- **information on customers:** including past purchases, account numbers and personal details such as home addresses, e-mail addresses and phone numbers
- **information on suppliers:** including contact details, items supplied, delivery dates and cost
- **information on stock:** material quantities, tools and equipment available
- **information on finished products:** products complete and stored ready for delivery to customers.

Within a database the data is sorted into a number of **records**. Each record contains a number of **fields** and it is within these fields that the data is stored. For example:

Table1 : Table

Field Name	Data Type	
Name	Text	
Address	Text	
Town / City	Text	
Country	Text	
Postcode	Text	
Phone Number	Number	
Job Title	Text	
Company Department	Text	

This is from a database program called Microsoft Access

The previous diagram shows the fields being set up within the **design view**. They can be modified to hold data such as text, number, currency, date, time, yes/no or even a hyperlink.

Once the fields are set up in the design view they can be viewed as a table (as shown below). It is at this point that data can be entered to form records – in this case the records are a company's employee details.

File Edit View Insert Format Records Tools Window Help				
ID	**Name**	**Address**	**Town / City**	**Country**
1	Tickle John	11 Red Road	Lincoln	England
2	Knoxville Jonny	4 Blue Street	Edinburgh	Scotland
3	Rowland Kelly	9 Mauve Close	Cardiff	Wales

Another view which is often used is the **form view**. The same data is displayed, although in a more attractive and accessible way. One record at a time is displayed (in this case John Tickle), with the fields being spaced and formatted as required.

Buttons can be added to the form, which can be used to carry out common database functions such as adding and deleting records, finding a record or printing a record.

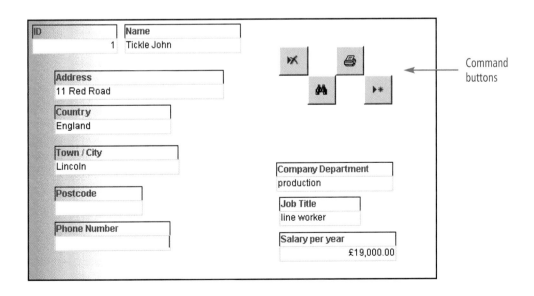

Command buttons

Database management systems

The **database management system (DBMS)** is a special program stored within the computer, which keeps track of where the information is stored and indexed so that users can quickly locate the information they require.

Task performed by the DBMS include:

- adding new records
- deleting unwanted records
- amending records already contained within the database
- linking or cross-referencing records to find information
- searching or sorting the database to find exact data
- printing records.

A common database management system has already been mentioned – Microsoft Access.

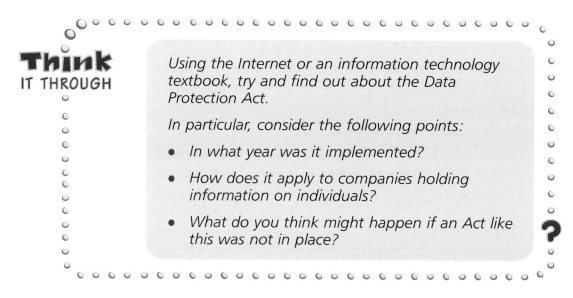

Think
IT THROUGH

Using the Internet or an information technology textbook, try and find out about the Data Protection Act.

In particular, consider the following points:

- *In what year was it implemented?*
- *How does it apply to companies holding information on individuals?*
- *What do you think might happen if an Act like this was not in place?*

Example

Some companies might have several databases, each containing very different information used for specific purposes.

For example, a car manufacturer might have the following databases:

- a product database containing records of each vehicle model that has been manufactured. It might include engine size, colour and any extras fitted such as alarms, CD player or a sunroof
- a manufacturing database containing records of all the components and materials used during manufacture. This list is often referred to as a 'bill of materials' or 'parts list'
- a customer database containing records of all the dealerships that have purchased cars. This would include chassis serial numbers so that the manufacturer knows

exactly what has been supplied to the customer. If there was a problem with a specific car, this database could be used to locate and recall it

- a spare parts database containing records of all spare materials and components required for servicing and replacing defective parts. This database would include what part of the store they were held in, and the quantity available.

The task of the DBMS is to co-ordinate all this information so that data can be cross-referenced between databases.

Spreadsheets

A spreadsheet is simply an organised way of allowing a user to enter and display information, carry out calculations and in some cases perform other functions such as displaying charts and graphs.

Each spreadsheet file contains a number of **worksheets** – individual pages containing **cells**, which hold the data. The worksheet cells are formatted into **rows** (running across, shown in red below) and **columns** (running down, shown in blue).

The most popular spreadsheet used today is Microsoft Excel, shown below.

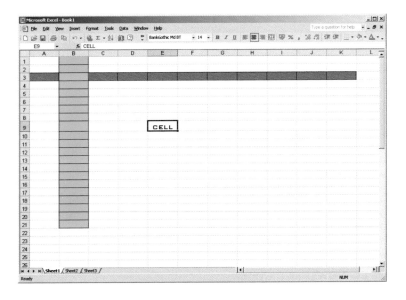

Spreadsheets are very useful for organising numerical data because the software is able to perform calculations – this explains their widespread use in the area of finance.

Popular applications of spreadsheets within manufacturing and engineering companies include profit/loss accounts, budget planning, project management and quality assurance recording.

One of the main advantages of spreadsheets is their ability to display data in a range of formats, including:

- table layout
- line graphs
- pie charts
- bar charts
- scattercharts (often used in quality assurance)
- area charts.

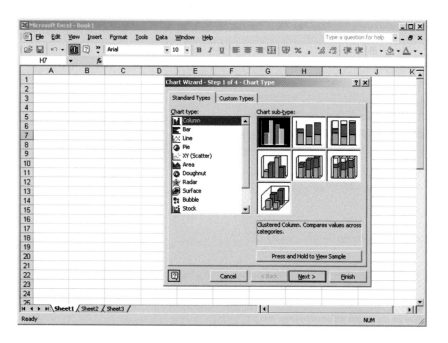

Other features of a spreadsheet include:

- you can insert, cut and paste information from other applications such as databases and wordprocessing packages
- formatting, such as changing row/column size, merging cells, adding colour and changing the font characteristics, is extremely easy
- unwanted information can be deleted and edited, copied or moved as required
- it is possible to search for key terms, filter and sort data into specific order – alphabetically, for example
- functions such as SUM, AVERAGE and IF can be used in calculations

- files can be transferred via e-mail to other individuals, departments or companies
- information from other worksheets can be used in calculations.

Example

Consider a fruit juice carton – before it is folded into shape it must first be cut to length.

A supplier of the material used to make the cartons has installed a quality system that ensures that the card is always cut to a specific length. The quality control department uses a spreadsheet to enter the cut-card length, analyse the results and to monitor if the process is 'in control'.

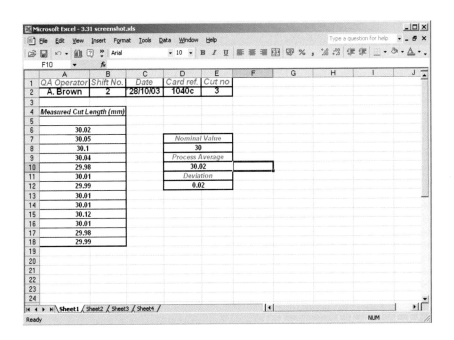

The **nominal value** is the ideal target value, which is manually entered by the QA (quality assurance) technician. The card is then automatically measured and the results inserted into the 'measured cut length' column of the spreadsheet.

The spreadsheet then calculates the average, which is then compared with the nominal value to produce a deviation value.

Any deviation below 0.5 mm is acceptable; hence this process, having a deviation of 0.02 mm, is in control.

The diagram on the next page shows the information displayed as a line graph to detail the fluctuations in the process – note the formulae for the simple calculations shown in the formulae bar.

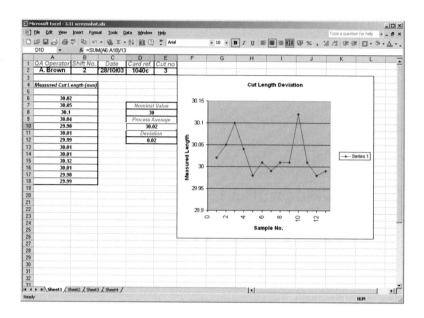

Think IT THROUGH

1 *Why would a company use a spreadsheet?*

2 *State an advantage of using spreadsheets.*

3 *Why would a company use a database?*

4 *With a database, what is the difference between cells, fields and records?*

THE JARGON DRAGON

infrastructure – the way in which communication is linked and organised

Telecommunications

Telecommunication is a term used to describe the **infrastructure** that allows a range of information to be transferred from a source to a destination. This information could be sound (for example, a telephone conversation), text (such as e-mail), graphics (web pages) or vision (TV programmes).

Telecommunications include communication by conventional wires (or lines), cables, radio, satellite and optical technology.

Devices such as mobile phones and modems for computer Internet access are common examples of telecommunications products.

Cables and wires

Traditional cables and wires are generally made up of copper insulation with a PVC coating. This is the type of wire used to carry electricity in your home – it connects all your plug sockets and light switches to the main electrical supply. It is also used to carry electricity to most home appliances – your microwave, toaster, TV and DVD player all use this type of wire.

Traditionally, all phone lines consisted of this type of cable, but many have since been replaced with more modern technology.

Coaxial cables have a clear plastic core surrounded by a PVC coating. They are used for a range of cables used in the broadcasting industry, including satellite and television leads. Telecommunications companies such as BT, Telewest and NTL also use this type of cable to connect your home phone line to the connection box in the street.

An **optical fibre** is a long, thin strand of very pure glass enclosed in an outer protective jacket – you may have seen these as Christmas decorations or in novelty gadget shops!

They work using light, which is internally reflected along the fibre at 200 million m/s (two-thirds the speed of light in a vacuum).

To establish a data link using optical fibre a transmitter/receiver unit must be set up at each end. This transmitter/receiver sends and recognises pulses of light from a light-emitting diode (LED) that is triggered by current from a computer interface.

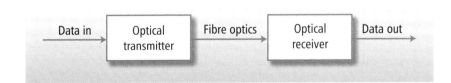

Data in → Optical transmitter → Fibre optics → Optical receiver → Data out

Fibre optics are also used for decorative products such as lights. The changing colours of the light travel down the glass fibres making them appear to change colour

Radio waves

You've probably heard of FM radio and AM radio – just look on your midi system – these are two examples of **radio waves**.

Radio waves are used to transmit music, conversations and other information though the air. They travel in waves that

oscillate many times per second. The number of oscillations (or cycles) per second completed by a radio wave is termed its **frequency**, and that frequency is measured in **hertz**.

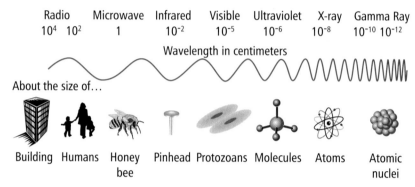

Radio	Microwave	Infrared	Visible	Ultraviolet	X-ray	Gamma Ray
10^4 10^2	1	10^{-2}	10^{-5}	10^{-6}	10^{-8}	10^{-10} 10^{-12}

Wavelength in centimeters

About the size of…

Building Humans Honey bee Pinhead Protozoans Molecules Atoms Atomic nuclei

Although radio waves are light waves, we cannot see them; the human eye is unable to detect light at a frequency lower than that of visible light. Therefore even though radio waves are all around us they are invisible and cannot be seen.

Other light waves that cannot be seen include ultraviolet (used for sunbeds and sterilising in hospitals), infrared (used in remote controls and burglar alarms) and X-rays (used widely in medicine).

Example

If you are ever listening to Radio One and hear Chris Moyles, Jo Wylie or Vernon Kay say 'you are listening to Radio 1 – 97–99 FM' the information they are giving you is the radio transmission frequency.

'97–99 FM' means that they are transmitting at between 97 MHz and 99 MHz. At 98 MHz, the transmitter at the radio station is transmitting at 98,000,000 cycles per second. To listen to these radio waves requires a frequency modulator (FM) – this is used to tune in to this particular frequency and produce a clear reception.

The main types of radio waves used for communicating are:

- **very low frequency (VLF):** used for long-distance communications over thousands of kilometres
- **low frequency (LF):** used in Europe for long-wave broadcasting
- **medium frequency (MF):** also known as medium wave, is used for broadcasting throughout the world

- **high frequency (HF):** HF or short wave has many applications, including broadcasting and long-distance (worldwide) communications
- **very high frequency (VHF)**
- **ultra high frequency (UHF):** used for both broadcasting and mobile communications, mainly over short distances (typically up to 100 km or more).

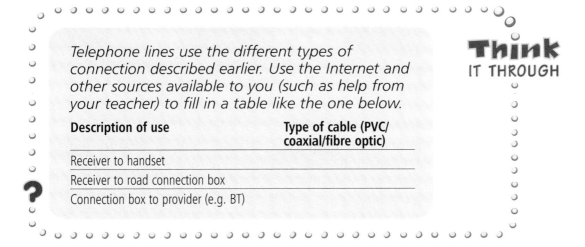

Telephone lines use the different types of connection described earlier. Use the Internet and other sources available to you (such as help from your teacher) to fill in a table like the one below.

Think
IT THROUGH

Description of use	Type of cable (PVC/ coaxial/fibre optic)
Receiver to handset	
Receiver to road connection box	
Connection box to provider (e.g. BT)	

The Internet

Take a look at the picture opposite. It's likely that although you would probably recognise film stars such as Brad Pitt or Russell Crowe, footballers such as Michael Owen, or pop stars such as Kylie, it's unlikely that you'll recognise this man. Yet he has had more impact on our daily lives over the past ten years than any of the other people mentioned above. We'll come to how he has achieved this later on.

Although the terms 'Web' and 'Internet' are often used together, they actually have two very different meanings.

The **Internet** is the global network that links computers worldwide. It carries data and makes the exchange of information possible.

The **(World Wide) Web** is a subset of the Internet. It is a collection of inter-linked documents that work together using common codes and language. This enables it to display material, which you know as web pages.

The Internet, therefore, consists principally of the hardware such as the modems, cables and wires that link our computers together as shown at the top of the next page.

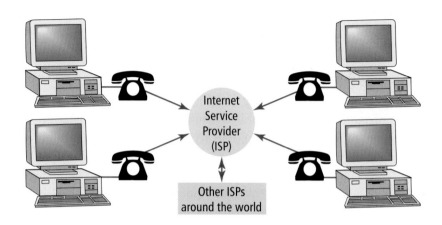

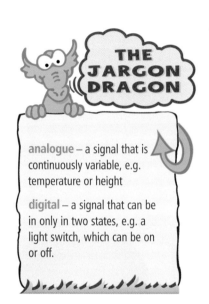

THE JARGON DRAGON

analogue – a signal that is continuously variable, e.g. temperature or height

digital – a signal that can be in only in two states, e.g. a light switch, which can be on or off.

Telephone lines were originally designed for speech, which is transmitted in **analogue**, or wave, form. In order for **digital** data (which the Internet uses) to be sent over a telephone line, it must first be converted to analogue form and then converted back to digital at the other end. This is achieved by means of a modem (MOdulator/DEModulator) at either end of the line.

The Internet has actually been around since 1969 where it was called the ARPANET – this was an acronym for the Advanced Research Projects Agency Network – and consisted of four computers. It was primarily used by scientists to transfer technical information from one to another.

It wasn't until 1990 that the Internet and WWW as we know it really took off, all thanks to one man. In March 1989, Tim Berners-Lee, an Oxford graduate and European physicist, proposed the idea of the World Wide Web as a means to better communicate research ideas amongst members of a widespread organisation. Berners-Lee (whose picture is shown on the previous page) went on to create the codes that we use today, and what's more he did it all for free. He invented the Web and simply gave it to the world.

The code used to link all the documents is called **hypertext transfer protocol (HTTP)**. This is a way of organising information so that both the sender and the receiver can understand it.

Websites are made up of a collection of web pages. These individual web pages are written in 'hypertext markup language' (HTML). The HTML tells Web browsers such as Navigator or Explorer how to display the various elements of a web page.

For example, this is the Sony web page as it appears to you:

This is the HTML used to make up the page:

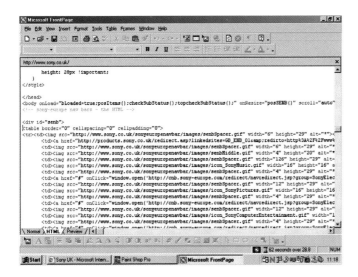

Internet service providers (ISPs) are responsible for enabling us to use the Internet – they are companies such as BT, AOL, NTL and Virgin.

The ISPs assign each computer a specific number called an **Internet Protocol (IP) address**. This is used to distinguish between individual computers using the net. Depending on the ISP you use and the contract that you have, you may have a permanent IP address or a different (dynamic) address each time you use the net.

Every web page on the Internet has its own unique address, known as a **uniform resource locator (URL)**. The URL tells a browser exactly where to go to find the page or object that it has to display. A well-known URL is http://www.ask.com.

How the Internet helps business

So how does the Internet help companies and businesses today?

Companies today generally use the Internet and WWW for various reasons. They include:

- marketing and advertising their company and products
- providing contact details and technical information to customers
- searching for and buying raw materials from suppliers
- selling products directly to customers.

Example

Take a look at the website below. It was designed by a GCSE engineering student and represents a fictional engineering fabrication company.

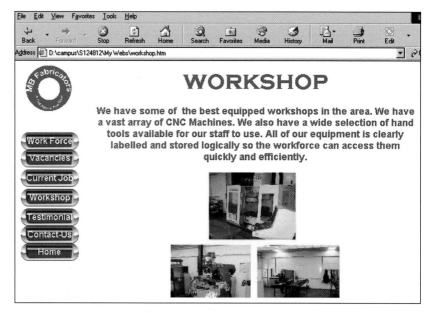

It features a homepage with company information, a logo and photographs. Within the homepage there are hyperlinks to other web pages:

- a staff organisation chart providing information on the staff and their roles and responsibilities
- a product page advertising the range of components fabricated in the past – in this case a screwdriver, hacksaw and mallet
- a manufacturing page showing the workshop and links to other sites
- a page about quality and how the company is responsible for producing quality products made to exact specifications.

Take a look at any company website. Note down the different pages, how they are linked together and what information they contain. Consider why each page contains that information and what the company is trying to achieve by placing it there.

Think IT THROUGH

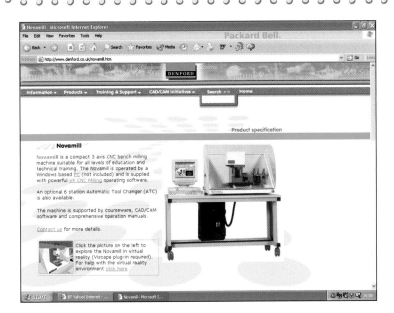

Electronic mail

Electronic mail, or **e-mail**, is arguably one of the most important developments in communication since the evolution of the mobile phone. It allows you to send messages, letters, documentation and various files by typing in the receiver's e-mail address and simply hitting the send button.

E-mail can be sent worldwide using the Internet or within an organisation by using an **intranet**.

Some advantages of e-mail include:

- a message can be sent to each person in a group of individuals at the same time
- at its quickest, e-mail takes only a few seconds to arrive at the recipient's inbox
- other files can be attached to a message (such as Word documents, spreadsheets and images)
- messages are saved automatically, and can be copied and printed for reference.

THE JARGON DRAGON

intranet – an internal network of computers, usually within a business, school, college or other medium to large organisation

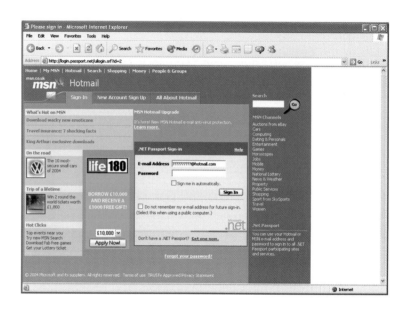

A popular way to send e-mail is by using the World Wide Web, for example Hotmail. You may use Hotmail to e-mail your friends, but it has many of the functions of more commercial e-mail packages. Hotmail allows you to send and receive messages, save and delete messages and attach documents such as JPEG pictures.

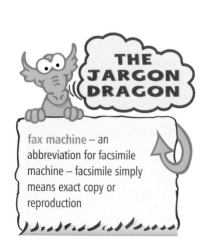

THE JARGON DRAGON

fax machine – an abbreviation for facsimile machine – facsimile simply means exact copy or reproduction

Before e-mail, manufacturing and engineering companies had to correspond by typing memos, sending information by external/internal post or by using **fax machines**. These techniques have several disadvantages:

Depending on the quality of delivery, posting information can take from an hour up to several weeks. Think of a company department based in Japan having to send a technical drawing to another department based in Scotland – this may take a few weeks to arrive! If the drawing was required urgently then this could cost the company valuable time and money.

While fax machines are much quicker than using the post, they depend largely on the quality of:

a the original document being sent
b the equipment being used.

Both these need to be of good quality in order to ensure good quality reproduction of the original document.

Companies can now use e-mail to arrange meetings, send minutes of meetings, issue memos, and send technical information, engineering drawings and quality information.

New materials and components

Introduction

The ongoing development of modern materials and components is closely linked to the manufacturing and engineering of exciting new products.

The development of materials dates way back, before 4000 BC, when metallic elements such as gold, tin and copper were first used for jewellery. The arrival of civilisations such as the Egyptians, Ancient Greeks and the Roman Empire further advanced the development of materials.

The Egyptians had a well-known association with ceramics – just think of the vast stone building blocks making up the pyramids. The ancient Greeks also used many ceramics, for fine pottery and porcelain.

The Romans used a diverse range of materials – metals such as lead, wrought iron and bronze were used in the military for weapons; gold and silver were used for jewellery; and ceramics such as marble and stone were used to create the vast structures, amphitheatres and buildings making up Ancient Rome. There is even evidence of an early composite being used, i.e. concrete (a combination of stone and cement), to provide strength within buildings.

In the Middle Ages the development of many metals continued. These included iron, bronze, steel and zinc for metalworking, armour and coins.

The Industrial Revolution (1750–1850) was a key part of history for engineering. Many processes were developed around this time, such as extrusion, rolling, drawing and casting, all to process new steels and irons available due to advances within materials science. The first **polymers** (plastics and rubber) were also developed around this time.

Arguably the most widespread development of materials occurred within the latter half of the twentieth century (1940 onwards). New metals were developed, such as aluminium alloys (used to make cars, aircraft, soft drinks cans, etc.); advanced polymers such as PVC and ABS; composites such as glass fibre; and new micro-electronics leading to advanced integrated circuits, an example being the Pentium microchips used so commonly today in computer design. Each of these new materials is discussed within this section.

Metals

Metals are usually combinations of metallic elements found naturally here on Earth. Common metallic **elements** used to make natural metals include gold, silver, tin, lead, iron, zinc and copper.

Alloys are metals that combine several different elements to make one material – good examples are brass (which is a combination of copper and zinc) and bronze (a mixture of copper and tin).

As discussed in Unit 2, metals are extremely good conductors of electricity and heat, are strong and yet can be shaped, which accounts for their extensive use in manufacturing and engineering.

Many metals, such as gold, tin and copper, have been used for thousands of years. Others, however, were developed quite recently. These include the following.

Aluminium alloys

Aluminium alloys possess high strength-to-weight ratios and have good resistance to **corrosion**. Aluminium alloys are very common and can be found as food packaging (cans and foil), in transport such as cars, aircraft and motorbikes, in buildings and as consumer goods such as furniture and kitchen appliances.

Magnesium alloys

Magnesium alloys are used, for example, in aircraft, golf clubs, printing machinery components, power tools and bicycles. Magnesium is often used as an alloy for parts that require good strength and are lightweight.

Nickel-based alloys

Discovered in 1751, nickel is a major alloying metal used to increase strength, toughness and resistance to corrosion.

Nickel alloys are used in a diverse range of products, including food-handling equipment, aircraft engines, nuclear power stations and coins.

Titanium alloys

Titanium alloys tend to be expensive and are therefore generally found only in very high performance products such as Formula One racing cars, aircraft engines, petrochemical and submarine parts.

Like many of the other alloys, titanium has high strength-to-weight ratio and excellent corrosion resistance.

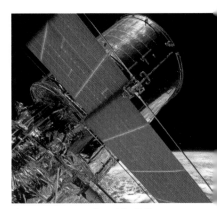

The extreme strength and flexibility of alloys like titanium make them ideal for use in hostile environments such as outer space

ductility – the ability of a material to be pulled and formed into a desired shape without breaking or fracturing

Stainless steel

Developed in the twentieth century, stainless steel is a combination of steel (iron and carbon) with other alloying elements such as nickel, molybdenum, manganese, aluminium and, most importantly, chromium.

Often used to make cutlery, kitchen sinks and domestic utensils (sieves, whisks, drainers, etc.), stainless steel has an excellent resistance to corrosion, good **ductility** and high strength.

Smart materials

Smart materials are designed to change their properties, structure or function when exposed to certain environmental changes. For example a novelty mug that changes colour when hot water is poured into it is a type of smart material.

Photochromic materials change colour when light is applied because of a change that takes place on a molecular level – the molecules react with the light causing a change in colour. These types of materials are often used in special paints and inks.

Thermochromic materials change colour when exposed to heat – the mug mentioned above is an example of such a material. Again, this type of material is often used in paint, inks and other applications.

Piezoelectric materials have two unique characteristics which make them useful when used in devices such as sensors:

- in some cases they are capable of exhibiting a change in size when an electric current is passed through
- alternatively when deformed they can give off a small but useful electrical discharge.

The application of heat turns these thermochromic dots orange

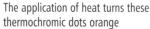

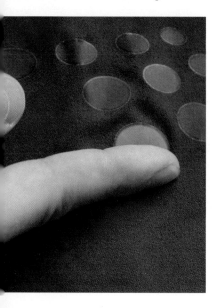

Piezoelectric materials are commonly used in car airbags. The material senses the force of an impact and sends an electric charge to inflate the airbag.

Shape memory alloys

Shape memory alloys are metals that can be formed into a shape at room temperature and will retain that particular shape. Once heated to a higher temperature, the material will 'remember' its original shape and deform back.

A combination of titanium and nickel produces a shape memory alloy.

Today and the future

Many of the developments in materials have been fuelled by the aerospace industry where it has been necessary to develop materials with very specific properties. These properties include high strength-to-weight ratios, making them very strong yet light, and a good level of resistance to corrosion and repetitive stresses such as **fatigue**.

Technology today allows us to produce a specific metal by combining various elements, with the finished metal having the desired characteristics of each individual element. This 'tailoring' allows batches of a unique metal to be made, specifically designed for maximum performance within a product.

THE JARGON DRAGON

fatigue – a form of material failure that is often caused by repetitive, cyclic stress – it often causes cracking of a component

Polymers

Polymers include the widely used materials plastic and rubber.

Many polymers are organic compounds based on carbon, hydrogen and other non-metallic elements. They are characteristically easy to shape, possess low mass, and many are extremely flexible.

Some of the numerous products manufactured from polymers include food and drink containers, packaging, housewares, clothing, paint, toys, computer products and car parts.

The first plastics were made from animal and vegetable products, **celluloid** (used in photographic film) being an early example. The first artificial, or synthetic, polymer was developed in 1906. It was called Bakelite and was used extensively to make telephone casings.

In 1920, the first modern plastic material was developed. Scientists extracted the raw material required to make plastics from **fossil fuels** such as coal and petroleum. Ethylene (used to make a popular plastic, polyethylene) was the first of such materials to be made, by reacting first coke and methane and then combining the product with hydrogen.

Put simply, polymers are long chains of molecules made by linking and cross-linking small repetitive groups of atoms, known as **monomers**.

The term 'poly' derives from the Greek meaning 'many' – hence many units of atoms.

Plastics are often sub-divided into two groups – **thermosetting** and **thermoplastic**. Thermosets retain their shape upon reheating while thermoplastics become pliable and can be reset. Thermoplastics are the most commonly used plastics for domestic products.

Popular examples of thermoplastics are:

- **PVC (polyvinyl chloride):** used to make window frames, insulation for wiring, floor tiles and garden hoses
- **nylon:** used to make bearings and gears which are often found in electrical equipment with moving parts – for example, printers and video recorders
- **polycarbonate:** used to make safety helmets, lenses and as a base for photographic film
- **acrylonitrile-butadiene-styrene (ABS):** used for car parts, toys and as casings for electronic products such as digital cameras, CD players and mobile phones
- **polyethylene:** used to make drinks bottles, toys and clear film used as food wrapping
- **polystyrene:** used as packing (in its foam state), toys and CD cases.

Examples of thermosets are:

- **silicone:** used to make fillers and sealants for bathroom furniture
- **polyesters:** used to make chairs, car parts and as a base for glass fibre

Which plastics are used in the construction of a motorcycle crash helmet?

- **epoxies:** used to make sinks and shower trays and electrical mouldings such as plugs and sockets.

Composites

Composites are combinations of different types of materials mixed together. The final material has the best characteristics of each of the original materials.

A common group of composites is also called **'reinforced plastics'**. These materials are made by placing dispersed fibres within a selected plastic material known as the **matrix**. Fibres commonly used include glass, carbon and boron.

Glass fibre is a familiar example, in which fibres of glass are embedded within a polymer. This type of reinforced plastic provides the material with the strength of the glass and the flexibility of the polymer.

Carbon fibre is also often used to make products that require flexibility yet high strength, for example fishing rods and golf clubs.

Concrete is another example of a composite material. Cement; sand and gravel are combined to make the final product.

Think IT THROUGH

Identify the type of material and name of material for the products within the table below. For example, the first product is a can of Fanta. This is made from a metal called aluminium.

Product	Type of material	Name of material
Fanta can	Metal	Aluminium
Car tyre		Vulcanised rubber
DVD player casing		ABS
Digital camera casing		
Adjustable spanner	Metal	
Safety hat		
CD cover	Polymer	
Mountain bike frame		
Car engine casing		
Snowboard		Glass fibre

Selection of materials

In conclusion, with so many new materials available, how do engineers actually select a material for a particular function?

Generally, they apply the following rules:

1 The properties of the materials, such as hardness, strength, weight, ductility and conductivity, are usually the first consideration. For example, a computer casing needs to be rigid, with good resistance to electricity and heat; hence a plastic such as ABS is often used.

2 Cost and availability are also important considerations. A readily available material such as iron makes carbon steel relatively cheap. However, a metal such as titanium, which is less common, has a higher price tag. The mass processing of plastics such as nylon and PVC make these materials also relatively inexpensive.

3 When consumers buy products (especially those for domestic use) they are often influenced by their appearance – also called **aesthetics**. Materials such as plastics are very easy to colour and naturally have a smooth finish. They are therefore commonly used on many domestic appliances, children's toys and electrical equipment.

In addition to these general rules, manufacturers take into account many other factors when choosing materials. These include:

- the cost of the manufacturing processes to be used, for example casting, machining and joining
- whether the material can be processed by a particular method
- the disposal and recycling of waste materials, especially in the chemical and biological, electronic and automotive industries.

Electronic components

Introduction
Advances in electronic components have made possible the development of many consumer products we take for granted today. As electronic components become increasingly more

complex and miniature in size, newer, improved products are constantly hitting the marketplace.

Think of the improvements in mobile phones and games consoles over the past few years. These have been made possible by the tiny components transforming stored energy from a battery or power cable into the sound waves used in your phone or the video game you see on your TV screen.

Some of the most important of these components are described below.

Resistors

A resistor is a device that doesn't allow current to flow as well as a normal length of wire. It resists the flow of current, hence the name. Resistance is measured in **ohms**. The higher the ohm value, the more it resists the flow of current. Resistors come in values from 0.1 ohm to 10 mega ohms (ten million ohms).

Capacitors

A capacitor is an electronic device used for storing electric charge. It works in the same way as a tank used to store water – when needed, it releases the required amount of charge into the circuit.

The units of capacitance are **farads**. A farad is a very large amount of capacitance, so submultiples such as microfarads (10^{-6}) and picofarads (10^{-9}) are used.

THE JARGON DRAGON

farad – the unit for measuring capacitance, named after the scientist Michael Faraday

ohm – the unit for measuring resistance, named after the mathematician Georg Simon Ohm

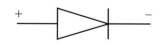

Diodes

A diode is a semi-conducting device, which allows electricity to flow in only one direction but not the other. It is like a one-way valve for electricity.

By looking at the symbol, you can see that it has the shape of an arrow. The electrical current will flow in the same direction as the arrow.

There are special terms used for each side of the diode – the positive side of the diode is called the **anode**. The negative side is called the **cathode**. Current always flows from the anode to the cathode.

LEDs

LED stands for light-emitting diode. An LED is a diode with a unique property – when electricity flows through it, it emits light. The LED requires only a small amount of voltage to operate and so it is used in electronics more often than light bulbs.

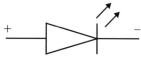

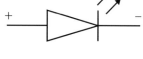

The circuit symbol for an LED has an anode and a cathode, as on a regular diode, but you know that it is an LED from the little arrows pointing away from it. This represents light energy being emitted.

Batteries

A battery is made up of two or more cells. Batteries supply voltage to a circuit which is used to drive the electric current around. They have two terminals; one terminal is marked (+), or positive, while the other is marked (−), or negative.

Electrons collect on the negative terminal of the battery. If a wire is connected between the negative and positive terminals, the electrons will flow from the negative to the positive terminal.

Inside the battery itself, a chemical reaction produces the electrons. The speed of electron production by this chemical reaction (the battery's **internal resistance**) controls how many electrons can flow between the terminals. Electrons flow from the battery into a wire, and must travel from the negative to the positive terminal for the chemical reaction to take place. That is why a battery can sit on a shelf for a year and still have plenty of power – unless electrons are flowing from the negative to the positive terminal, the chemical reaction does not take place. Once you connect a wire, the reaction starts.

Variable resistors

Variable resistors have a dial or a knob that allows you to change the resistance. Volume controls are variable resistors. When you change the volume you are changing the resistance, which changes the current. Making the resistance higher will let less current flow so the volume goes down. Making the resistance lower will let more current flow so the volume goes up.

Wire

Wire is used to electrically connect circuit parts, devices, equipment, etc. There are various kinds of wiring materials. Materials with good electrical conductance are always used, for example copper. On printed circuit boards (PCBs) connections are made by copper tracks which connect all the components. On small circuits these tracks are incredibly small and intricate.

Lamps

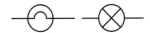

Lamps are used as indicators and for illumination. The most common type used has a filament coil which glows white hot when a current passes through it. The filament is in a space filled with an **inert gas** to aid the light output and to prevent corrosion of the filament. Bulbs use more power than LEDs but give a higher light output.

They are fixed into place with either a bayonet or screw cap fitting – both are very common.

Motors

A motor is a device for changing electrical energy into movement. The turning power (or **torque**) of a motor can vary greatly. Generally, small motors have low torque whereas large motors usually have a high torque rating. Motors come in AC and DC versions. DC types of 3–12 volts are the most suitable for general use.

Transformers

A transformer is made from two coils, one on each side of a soft iron core. It can decrease the voltage (called a step-down transformer) or increase the voltage (called a step-up transformer).

Transformers are widely used as part of the power supply to electrical equipment. Look on your printer or games console power lead – the larger plastic part houses the transformer.

Transistors

In electronics, signals sometimes need to be **amplified** (increased in magnitude). Take, for example, a mobile phone – the signal from the aerial is relatively weak and needs to be boosted so that it can be heard on the speaker. The component used to do this is a transistor.

There are two basic types of transistor: the n-p-n type and the p-n-p type. These vary according to the configuration of the materials used to produce them, which in turn affects the direction of current flow.

A transistor has three main parts: the collector (of the current), the base (which amplifies the signal) and the emitter (of the amplified signal). These are the three 'legs' of the transistor, as shown in the photograph below.

Integrated circuits

Integrated circuits, or ICs, are extremely small circuits containing resistors, diodes, transistors, connections and other components. These circuits are contained within a single 'chip' of a semi-conductor material, typically silicon. ICs can be made using chemical and microphotography techniques that are carried out automatically at a relatively small cost.

Before the invention of ICs in around 1960, circuits were much larger and more expensive, and consisted of various standard-sized components. ICs revolutionised the electronics industry and can be found in just about any electronic product – phones, calculators, digital cameras, computers, DVD players and MP3 players all contain integrated circuits.

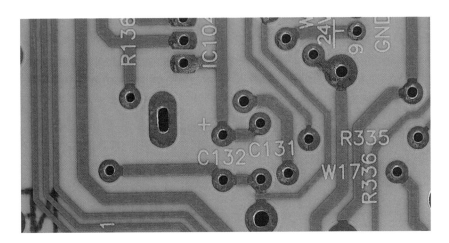

PCBs

Printed circuits boards (PCBs) are used to connect and hold electronic components together in one rigid structure.

Just about every electrical product manufactured today has a PCB inside it – from the relatively simple circuits in kettles or toasters to the highly technical models used in computer equipment.

PCBs are usually manufactured from board or plastic composites. The most common material used is glass fibre because of its excellent strength, resistance to electrical current and corrosion.

PCBs are made using a combination of photographic and chemical processes. These are used to print the copper tracks, which connect the components. A solder-resistant layer and text notation is usually also added via a printing process. A punching or CNC process is then used to achieve their final shape.

PCBs can be manufactured relatively easily in large quantities, which make them an invaluable part of many products in the marketplace.

Automated assembly of printed circuit boards

Components are usually applied to PCBs using highly sophisticated pick-and-place robotics, auto-insertion machines or by manual labour.

PCBs that are assembled using pick-and-place robotics are often described as using 'surface mount technology'. The robots are programmed by an operator 'teaching' a microcomputer (within the machine) where and how the parts should be placed. The machine then loads the PCB, repeats the program and applies the components in the correct orientation and sequence.

Auto-insertion works in much the same way although it is used for components with legs. The legs are pushed into holes (previously drilled within the PCB) and are bent round and cut to size to secure a good fit to the PCB.

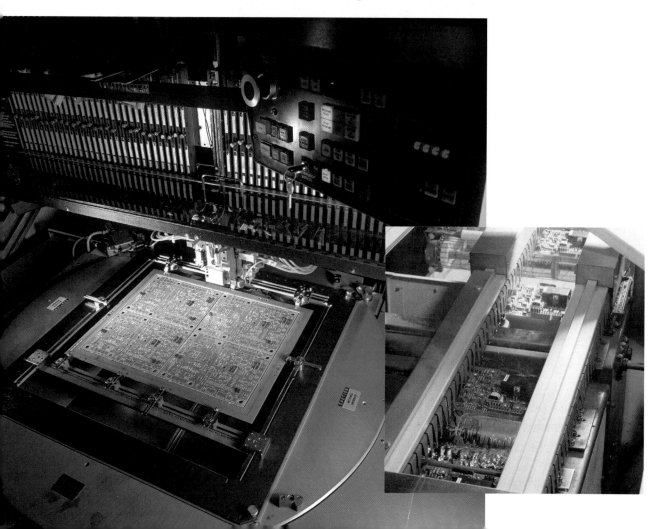

Systems and control technology

Introduction

Until the 1950s most manufacturing operations were carried out using traditional machinery such as milling machines and presses, which were worked manually. As new complex products were developed it meant the operators struggled to make parts that were exactly alike, and often several trial-and-error attempts had to be made to get it right. The word 'automation' (meaning self-acting) was derived in the mid-1940s by the US automobile industry to indicate 'automatic handling of parts between production machines'.

These highly mechanised machines often required people with special expertise to set them up, and they were used only for producing very high volume, mass-produced products such as cars. This continued for several years until the development of the first computers.

During the 1960s the introduction of computers was a major factor in the development of automation. Computerised technology led to computer numerical control (CNC), automated material handling, industrial robots, computer-aided design (CAD), computer-aided manufacturing (CAM), computer-aided engineering (CAE), and computer-integrated manufacturing (CIM).

CAD, CAM and CNC have all been discussed earlier in the book. Now we shall look at the other terms listed above.

Computer-aided engineering (CAE) is a term commonly used to encompass CAD, CAM and CNC. It therefore refers to the design, 3D modelling, scientific analysis and processing of a product.

Materials handling

Materials handling/transfer is the process used to transport parts and materials between workstations and assembly points.

Conveyors

A common type of transfer machine is the **conveyor** – you may have seen conveyors in the airport, at the check-in desk or when collecting your luggage. You may also have seen them at the check-out at the supermarket.

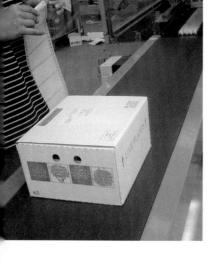

A belt conveyor

manufacturing and engineering companies use conveyors to move parts around, therefore reducing the need for manual handling. Common types of conveyors are belt, roller, slat and overhead. They are usually powered using an electric motor connected to a drive mechanism.

Belt conveyors are generally used on assembly or packing lines. They are also often found in the food and pharmaceutical industries, which require very clean manufacturing environments.

Slat conveyors are often used where rapid speed and accuracy are required. Again, the pharmaceutical and food industries are the largest group of customers for this type of conveyor. The biggest advantage is that they can open up, which allows them to move around bends, and they can be washed down for hygiene purposes.

A slat conveyor

Roller conveyors are sometimes called gravity conveyors. They are generally used when transporting packaging such as plastic crates or cardboard boxes; consequently they are often found in the despatch department of a company.

A roller conveyor

Unlike other conveyor types, they usually do not rely on electrical power. Instead, the products are 'freewheeled' along the conveyor or slid down a slight drop, therefore using gravity to move the item.

Overhead conveyors are primarily used to save space. Most are electrically powered, but some use low-friction, free-running designs.

Overhead conveyors are widely used in the automotive industry, by cycle manufacturers, mail order companies and clothing manufacturers.

An overhead conveyor

Remotely operated/automated guided vehicles

Remotely operated vehicles (ROVs), sometimes called automated guided vehicles (AGVs), are normally used in larger manufacturing and engineering environments. They can be found predominantly in the aerospace, automotive and paper and board industries for handling materials and parts, and carrying out warehouse operations.

They are basically robot vehicles that move around automatically, without the need to be 'driven' by human operators. ROVs normally navigate by following a wire embedded in the floor of the factory, or by using a laser which detects their position based on specific points within the factory. They often form part of a complex manufacturing system in which they ensure that parts and materials arrive just as they are needed within the manufacturing process.

An example of an ROV is shown below:

Industrial robots

If you were asked, 'What is a robot?', the chances are that you would be thinking about one from a film or television.

Although such a robot may be fictional, robots in industry are very real.

The word 'robot' is simply a Czech word meaning 'worker'. First used in the early 1960s, early industrial robots were used to carry out hazardous operations such as handling toxic and radioactive materials. Industrial robots have since developed into multifunctional workers able to work with very high accuracy and repeatability. They have been defined as a 'reprogrammable, multifunctional manipulators, designed to move parts, tools or other specialist devices'.

Robots have been developed to use computer technology, and in 1974 the first robot controlled by a microcomputer was introduced. Robots are now very widespread in industry, and are used in:

- materials handling
- spot welding
- machining
- spray painting
- automated assembly.

Robots' components

The following diagram shows an articulated robot – this type of robot is very common in industry.

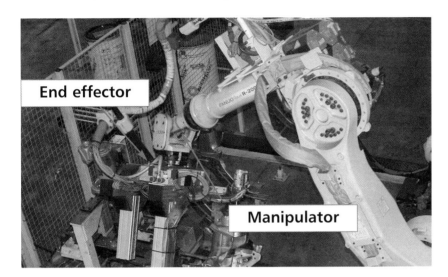

The **manipulator** is also called the 'arm and wrist'. This is because it provides motion similar to that of your arm and wrist. In the past, movement was made possible by mechanical devices such as gears and links; more modern robots use electric motors for more accurate control.

The **end effector** is basically the end-of-arm tooling. Depending on the function of the robot, it could be equipped with grippers, hooks, spray guns, power tools or more specific equipment such as materials handling fixtures.

The **power supply** provides the movement of the manipulator and end effector. The power supply for the robot in the photograph is electricity, although in some cases pneumatic (air pressure) and hydraulic (oil) power are used.

The **control system** communicates the instructions used to move the robot to its various components. This is essentially the brain of the robot, which tells the other components where and when to move.

The most common type of robot used in industry uses a control system termed 'playback'. This type of control allows the operator to 'teach' the robot the sequence of movements required to complete a processing operation. The robot then remembers these movements using co-ordinate points in various axes. When all the stages are complete, the robot can 'play back' the program and hence repeat the production task as many times as needed.

Programmable logic controllers – PLCs

PLCs are used in industry to control just about everything, from materials-handling conveyors to highly automated assembly equipment.

Example

A switch is required to turn on a conveyor belt motor and sound a bell to safely alert production staff after 10 seconds.

A simple external timer and bell could achieve this. However, if this switch had to control 20 conveyor belts then 20 timers would be needed – this would obviously require more setting up and additional cost to the company.

If a PLC was used, then it would use a program to switch all the motors on at the correct time. This program would control an internal set of instructions held within the PLC (in the CPU) called logic.

PLCs allow the programmer to wire up as many inputs (switches, sensors, etc.) and outputs (motors, lights, etc.) as required, and to control them by programming the unit with the required instructions or logic.

Before the introduction of PLCs in the late 1960s, such machinery was controlled using large, manually wired cabinets containing banks of wires, switches, relays and other components.

PLCs provide the same function but in a much smaller package. Roughly the size of a loaf of bread, the PLC contains the following key parts:

- **Central processing unit (CPU):** this controls all the PLC's activities in response to a program held in the memory.
- **Input cards:** these are the connections to external devices such as switches and sensors. They provide an input signal to the CPU.

- **Output cards:** these are also connections to external devices, but this time to the output components such as motors, lights or a siren.

Some advantages of PLCs are that:

- reprogramming is extremely easy compared with the manual rewiring of an entire cabinet
- they have extremely good repeatable operation – they don't seize or corrode like conventional components
- faultfinding can be carried out very easily.

Check out the website www.PLCS.net for more information.

Computer-integrated manufacturing (CIM)

CIM is the term used to describe the computerised connection of all aspects of design, planning, processing, distribution and management. It can be summarised in the diagram below. CIM is an integral part of many engineering activities and is vital in producing many of the quality products we use today.

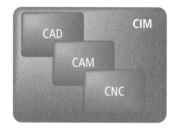

CAE (computer-aided engineering) can be described as an integrated process. The drawing is produced using CAD and then processed using a CAM package. The completed CAM file is then downloaded to a CNC machine which physically produces the product.

The table below provides an example of the use of CIM for each of the engineering sectors:

Sector	Example of CIM
Textiles and clothing	The CAE used to develop clothing pattern templates and then cut them out using specialist equipment
Food and drink	The control of highly complex conveyor systems used to transport food goods and ingredients
Printing and publishing	The use of desktop publishing linked to specialist photo equipment used to produce the printing press plates (see case study)
Engineering fabrication sheet	The use of CAD, CAM (CAE) and CNC to cut metal using laser and plasma-cutting equipment
Mechanical and automation	The control of robotics and ROVs
Electrical, electronic, computer and telecommunications	The design and control of the computer-controlled pick-and-place robotics used to place tiny electronic components on PCBs

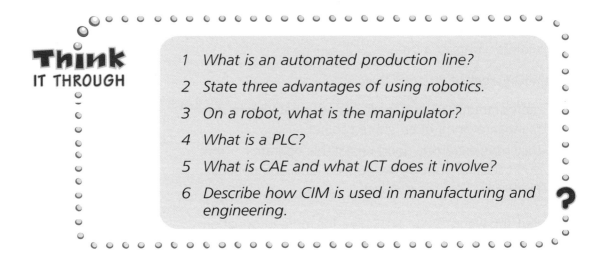

Think
IT THROUGH

1 What is an automated production line?

2 State three advantages of using robotics.

3 On a robot, what is the manipulator?

4 What is a PLC?

5 What is CAE and what ICT does it involve?

6 Describe how CIM is used in manufacturing and engineering.

Imagine a place – the size of a small town – where workers drive around on electric vehicles that hardly make a sound.

In this place vehicles can guide themselves and shuttle from place to place, picking up parts that automated machines and humans need to carry out their jobs.

Imagine a place where humans work alongside hundreds of robots. They are all working together to meet a specific objective.

Some of the robots even think for themselves.

This is the Nissan factory in the north-east of England.

Covering 3 million square metres, Nissan UK is based near Washington, employing around 5000 people and pumping £400 million a year into the local economy.

The plant is responsible for producing three different models of car for all of Europe and is capable of producing a car every 60 seconds.

With every individual car having approximately 5000 components, human workers need a little help.

In this case the help is in the form of nearly 1000 industrial robots carrying out a range of activities, including moving parts such as doors and bonnets, welding using high-precision tooling at extremely high temperatures, and spray painting.

case study

Nissan

Working at high speeds of up to 2 m/s (metres per second), they meticulously carry out their functions with an urgency that makes them seem almost alive. Often they work in very close proximity, passing parts to each other, with each robot completing its task and simply passing on the finished job to the next workstation.

At Nissan the robots are used to carry out work that requires heavy handling or operations – work that causes humans fatigue or repetitive strains.

As Chris Purnell (Training Controller) at Nissan states: 'We are getting much better at identifying operator concerns and using this type of technology to assist.'

The introduction of this technology allows human workers to be repositioned on operations that require adaptability and intricacy – operations in which the introduction of automation such as robotics would be uneconomical. Chris continues, 'We are not trying to replace people, robotics allows us to relocate workers to environments where they can be utilised fully'.

These robots aren't what most people would expect. Take for example the Fanuc 2000I – it stands over 3 m high when at full stretch and could punch straight through a car roof with ease. It can be programmed for a range of operations and is used primarily at Nissan to carry out spot welding on the car body shells. The electro-operated servo-welding guns used as the end effectors can be adjusted to the perfect welding distance. This ensures a high quality weld, and also preserves the life of the copper welding electrodes used to supply the high current to the weld.

Electrically powered, the control units for these robots are roughly the size of a fridge and use electric servo-motors to transfer movement to the manipulator and wrist.

Programming is carried out using handsets that are used by the operator to 'teach' each robot a variety of positional movements and actions. These are recorded by the robot and then played back and repeated in order to carry out the production operation.

Accurate to 0.3 mm, once programmed by the operator, the robot intelligently adapts the program to find the best sequence of movements, therefore reducing cycle times and saving valuable seconds.

In operation the robot provides feedback to the operator through the handset. Also, if a robot stops work for some reason, the robots that come after it on the production line recognise this and continue to work until they are unable to do so due to the lack of work being passed from the 'down' robot.

Nissan also uses a vast range of other control technology. Various components are carried to the manufacturing cells on the production line using conveyors, while overhead cradles are used to position the car assemblies.

Another form of materials handling is the use of automated guided vehicles. AGVs are used to transport components from stock to the appropriate manufacturing cell. They do this by following a wire embedded in the factory floor, which is detected by a sensor on the AGV.

AGVs are used to continuously carry wiring harnesses from a docking station to the production line.

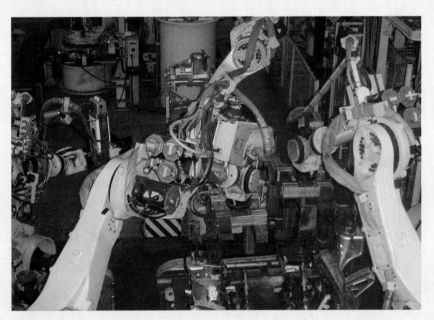

The sight of the robots working with such accuracy and repeatability is quite extraordinary and very impressive, perhaps best summarised by Chris Purnell:

'I've been round this place a hundred times and it is always inspirational to watch the robots at work ... I could watch them all day long.'

case study

Newspaper production

Most people would probably admit to taking a local newspaper for granted – it turns up on time, day after day, it is purchased for a relatively small price, it is read and then used for packing boxes or is discarded and hopefully recycled.

What many people would be surprised by is the amount of new technology and effort required to produce a local daily newspaper.

Take, for example, the *Hartlepool Mail*, which, every day, reaches 21,000 homes in the area, where it is read by approximately 60,000 people.

It is published six days a week and the company (which is owned by a larger business – the Edinburgh-based Johnston Press PLC) has a turnover of approximately £132 million.

When you walk into the printing department of the newspaper you are immediately struck by the amount of new technology being utilised. Overhead conveyors position what seems like an endless stream of paper into a highly automated printing press. The press then uses various cylinders applied with different-coloured inks (black, yellow, magenta and cyan) which roll over the paper, producing the full-colour images you see in the final newspaper. Each cylinder can be individually positioned to a fraction of a millimetre to ensure this 'layering' of colour is as exact as possible.

If you look at a colour newspaper, you will be able to see a cross toward the centre of the spread. This cross is the datum used to align the various cylinders – each individual cylinder prints an individual cross. If the cylinders are aligned correctly then you should see only one final cross.

The press can produce an impressive 45,000 newspapers per hour, which are then carried by a series of overhead, roller and slat conveyors to the despatch department to be 'shipped' into the surrounding communities.

Before the printing stage, there is a great deal of new technology used to produce the aluminium plates attached to the press cylinders and which apply the ink to the paper.

The process of producing the newspaper starts in the newsroom where the reporting staff combine local correspondence and photographs with national press stories wired in from news centres.

Using desktop computers, the stories and photographs are placed into templates where they are formatted and edited ready for printing. The software used is a publishing software package called Adobe InDesign.

If you open a newspaper, you will notice that the front and back pages are on the same piece of paper or 'spread', for example page 1 may be joined onto page 28. This is because of the way the computer file is imposed onto the aluminium printing plates – through a process called 'image setting'.

The completed publishing files are combined using 'speed drivers' to produce the different spreads used to make up the newspaper.

Once approved, this file is then transferred onto a special film (as shown below). Using a laser, the machine 'prints' the image and text onto the film, which is then developed, fixed, washed and dried using a series of chemical baths and water.

The negative film is then placed on a piece of equipment called an 'exposure frame machine' which transfers the desired image to the aluminium plate.

The dark parts of the film protect the plate from an ultraviolet light source, while the transparent parts allow the light to penetrate through to the special coating on the plate – this coating reacts to the UV light.

When developed, the exposed parts of the plate are darker and are fixed with the newspaper image (as shown below)

When the plate is attached to the printing press cylinders, the ink adheres only to the dark parts of the plate – as the paper is fed through the press the cylinders roll across, producing the final product.

The application of technology

Having read this unit you will now be in little doubt of the impact of technology on our daily lives.

The development of technology is driving forward constantly, allowing the ideas of manufacturers and engineers to be turned into innovative new products. Wherever you are now, simply look up and take a look round – manufacturing and engineering are evident everywhere. Your footwear and clothing, the food you eat and drink, the cars, motorbikes, cycles and lorries on the roads, video games, computers, DVD, video and midi equipment are all developed through the use of new technology.

You have learned how products can be grouped into six sectors:

- printing, publishing, paper and board
- food and drink, biological and chemical
- textiles and clothing
- mechanical and automotive
- electrical, electronic, computing and telecommunications
- engineering fabrication.

All of these sectors use new technology and advanced processing techniques to varying degrees.

You will also now be aware of the three main classifications of new technology.

Information and communications technology

Perhaps you have used some of this type of technology in the past – wordprocessing software to write letters and assignments, spreadsheets to carry out calculations and databases to store information. It is also likely that you have used e-mail to write to friends and the Internet to visit your favourite websites, and to download games and music.

You will now be aware of how industrial companies utilise this technology to aid and assist the manufacturing and engineering of products.

One of key elements of this category of new technology is computer-aided engineering, which includes the key innovations of computer-aided design (CAD) and computer-aided manufacturing (CAM).

Not many industries these days work without some type of CAD – it could be desktop publishing, the graphical design of food packaging, the highly complex technical drawings often used in electrical and electronic work or the component drawings so common in mechanical and automotive engineering.

Equally widespread is the use of CAM to help turn these highly technical drawings into actual products.

New materials and components

This second of the three categories of new technology is arguable the most important.

Humans have been developing new materials for thousands of years, dating right back to the first metals used by early civilisations. Constant progress has been made throughout history, notably by the Egyptians and Romans, and during the Middle Ages and the Industrial Revolution in the 1800s. However, no developments have moved as rapidly as in the last century.

The development of alloy metals, plastics and composites such as glass fibre underpin all of the new products we take for granted today.

The invention of the microchip not only led to the first home computers but was also key to the progress of automation, robotics and control technology used to manufacture many highly complex products. Microchips are now found in many home appliances, including video recorders, DVD players, microwaves and even some toasters and children's toys.

Control technology

The advancement of the final category, control technology, raises many issues regarding the disadvantages of new technology.

With highly automated production lines now used throughout the world to carry out manufacturing processing, questions inevitably arise regarding employment opportunities and the environmental issues associated with the use of new technology.

This is a highly complex issue and varies from one industry to another and from company to company – some of the key concerns are discussed below.

The environmental impact

In the past, manufacturing and engineering activities have contributed to many of the environmental problems that we are seeing today – the depletion of the ozone layer, global warming and acid rain – all due to high levels of water and air pollution.

Some scientists believe that these effects are so devastating that average global temperatures will rise by up to 6°C by the end of the century, heavy rain will cause river deposits to increase by up to 50% and the biggest floating ice sheets on Earth could melt, increasing seawater levels by 7 metres.

So what is being done about it? Industry today is still responsible for the emission of gases such as carbon monoxide and sulfur dioxide into the atmosphere, but the levels are monitored very closely by various environmental groups.

Waste products from older-style industrial plants like this one have had a massive impact on the environment

It is now well understood that waste materials are an inevitable aspect of manufacturing and engineering activities, and it is necessary to dispose of these materials in a safe and responsible manner. Metallic and non-metallic materials, oils, lubricants, scrap products and gases all require safe disposal, treatment or recycling. This is now governed by stringent and detailed international law. Choosing materials that can be safely recycled or disposed of is now a key feature of the design of any new product.

Consider a mobile phone – it contains a large range of materials, including copper, aluminum, ABS plastic and glass.

Key

Cu	copper (metal)
Al	aluminium (metal)
Fe	iron (metal)
PMMA	polymethyl methacrylate (polymer)
SiO_2	silicone dioxide (glass)
PC	polycarbonate (polymer)
Si	silicone (polymer)
POM	polyoxymethylene (polymer)
PS	polystyrene (polymer)
Ni	nickel (metal)
Sn	tin (metal)
ABS	acrylonitrile-butadiene-styrene (polymer)
TBBA	tetrabromobisphenol (polymer)
LCP	liquid crystal polymer

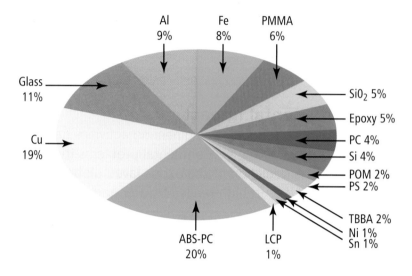

Today, typically between 65 and 80% of the materials used in a mobile phone can be recycled and reused. Furthermore, up to 90% of the plastics materials can be burnt in a furnace and used as fuel.

Manufacturing and engineering have no doubt damaged our planet over the past few hundred years since the evolution of mass production – it is how we proceed from now that will dictate the future of the environment.

The loss of employment opportunities

During the twentieth century, advances in automation have been blamed for the loss of employment in industries that depended heavily on large workforces – the car industry, for example.

Industrial robots do not need to take a break, they can work through the night and never get tired – consequently they have replaced the need for manual labour for many production activities. Machinery such as conveyor belts have reduced the need for manual material handling and CAD has been accused of reducing the level of job opportunities in technical design.

Whilst this is no doubt true, it is also necessary to consider the employment created by new technology. Advances in electronics, microelectronics and new technologies have resulted in new products, which have created vast ranges of job opportunities – ICT consistently proved the largest growing industry sector within the 1980s and 1990s.

It is highly unlikely that manual labour will ever be completely replaced in manufacturing. Many industries such as the textile, food and electronics sectors still place a great deal of importance on people power. As a workforce, people are able to learn quickly, and they can adapt to new skills that can be acquired and refined much faster than the automated equivalent.

Automation can be incredibly expensive to install and its introduction can usually be justified only in mass production, hence there will always be a need for manual labour in manufacturing and engineering.

In conclusion, then, how important is new technology?

You should be in little doubt that it is vital to maintain the standard and quality of living we take for granted in this country today. In order to do this, technology must continue to develop.

Advances are constantly being made in ICT, materials, new components and control technology, and the driving force behind these are the engineers who are designing, developing and manufacturing new products that hit the marketplace every day. If you complete this qualification and move on to choose a career in engineering, you too could become a part of this process.

case study

Textiles and clothing

Cross training shoes

Introduction

You would be hard pushed to find someone who doesn't own or hasn't in the past purchased a pair of training shoes. Used every day by athletes and sportsmen and women, as well as being a popular item of fashion clothing, the training shoe industry is worth billions of pounds worldwide each year.

A hugely competitive industry, the large manufacturers such as Nike, Adidas, Puma and Reebok pour millions of pounds into advertising each year to remain at the top of the industry.

Key parts

The key parts of a training shoe include:

- outsole (bottom of training shoe)
- midsole (cushioning part)
- upper (top of training shoe).

Key things to investigate

ICT

- Prominent in the manufacture of training shoes is the use of CAE. CAD is used to design, develop and produce 3D models of the training shoe. CAM and CNC are used to manufacture the mould used to produce the outsole and midsole rubber materials. CAE is also used to cut the patterns used for the uppers.

- One of the key ways ICT is used by training shoe companies is for advertising. Take a look at any of the websites in the 'Where to look' section – all use sophisticated graphics and represent state-of-the-art web design. Companies advertise using the Web, by sponsoring sportsmen and women, and on TV. All these advertising methods provide product awareness to the marketplace.

New materials and components
An interesting aspect of the design and development of cross training shoes is the use of new materials.

- Outsoles are typically made of extremely durable carbon rubber or a combination of blown rubber to provide a more flexible, lighter outsole.
- A polymer such as polyurethane is often used as the midsole to make a dense and durable cushioning material.
- The majority of training shoes utilise a leather upper, often combined with a synthetic lightweight mesh to allow the foot to breathe.

Systems and control technology
- The training shoe industry still uses high volumes of manual labour, so it tends to be largely based in Asia where labour costs are very competitive.
- Some of the systems and control technology used includes transfer machines and conveyors, and automatic cutting machines.

Where to look
Check out the following websites:

- Nike (www.nikebiz.com)
- Adidas (www.adidas.co.uk)
- Mizuno (www.mizunoeurope.com)

case study

Printing and publishing

Magazines

Introduction

Consumers buy millions of magazines each year in the UK. Some are printed weekly, some fortnightly others once a month.

The most popular types of magazines tend to be fashion, sport, culture, television guides or hobby-based reading.

Key things to investigate
ICT

ICT is used widely in the production of magazines. Two of the main examples are:

* Digital photography and text are combined using specialist publishing software – a form of computer-aided design.
* E-mail is used to communicate correspondence and in some cases articles and photographs produced by journalists who may not be based at the magazine headquarters.

Materials and components

Consider the grade and type of paper used. How does it differ from standard A4 in weight and composition?

Systems and control technology

The printing and publishing industry relies heavily on good quality printing presses. These are hugely automated, using different types of conveyors to transport the raw materials and finished product.

Where to look

- The 'British Printing Industries Federation' is a good place to start for information on this industry.
  (www.bpif.org.uk)

Google search topics

- printing processes
- industrial paper supply
- industrial printing

Printing and publishing

case study

case study

Food and drink

Bottled water

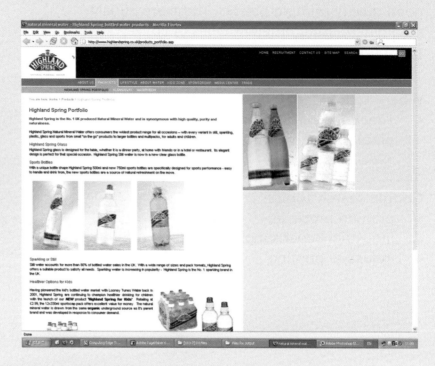

Introduction
You may think 'What's a bottle of water got to do with new technology?' and you would be asking yourself a perfectly reasonable question. However just because water is a natural product it doesn't mean that new technology isn't used at some point in its production.

Key things to investigate
ICT
ICT is used by the manufacturers of bottled water in several ways:

- Correspondence between company members is done via e-mail and the companies also have websites to promote their products.
- CAD is used to design the packaging and labels on the bottles – this is extremely important in developing an image which suggests a top quality product.
- The bottle is designed using CAE and utilises CNC machines to produce moulding tools used to manufacture the finished plastic parts.

New materials and components
The main ingredient is obviously water; naturally sourced from locations such as the French Alps.

Another main ingredient is a recyclable polymer such as polyethylene used in the manufacture of the bottles.

Systems and control technology
Despite producing a natural product, this industry is still heavily automated.

Advanced conveyor systems are used to transport the product to the various stages of bottling, filling and applying the bottle tops. Various types are used, such as roller and slat, which snake round in many different directions to transport the product from stage to stage.

Where to look
- The major manufacturers such as Highland Spring, Evian and Volvic have limited information on their websites – take a look as part of your research. (www.highlandspring.co.uk, www.evian.com and www.volvic.co.uk)
- A good place to find information on the types of conveyors used is the manufacturers – run a search on 'conveyor manufacturers'.
- www.isomaconveyors.co.uk and www.armax-conveyors.co.uk have some very good information.

case study

Mechanical/automotive sector

Car engine

Introduction

One of the key areas of this sector is transport manufacture – in the UK it is worth around £61 billion a year.

An essential part of any vehicle is the engine. The engine's function is to compress and ignite fuel, which produces the necessary drive to enable a vehicle to move.

Key parts

The key parts of an engine include:

- engine block
- pistons
- cam shaft with followers
- crank shaft
- cylinder head
- belts.

Key things to investigate
ICT

- CAE is extensively used in the design and manufacture of all engine components, and this is unquestionably the most important aspect of ICT used in the production of car engines.

- CAD is used to design the parts, at which point the design is transferred to CAM packages to assist in the process design.
- CNC is often used to design casting and moulding tools in addition to performing machining operations to exact specifications.

Materials and components

The principal group of materials used is the metals – to investigate further, look into aluminium alloys and carbon steel alloys.

Polymer materials such as rubber and ABS plastics are also used on many components.

Systems and control technology

With such high product volumes being manufactured in the car industry, many of the casting and forming processes used are automated and computer controlled.

To investigate further, look into modern casting and forming processes and computer-integrated measurement to check quality.

Where to look

Check out the major car manufacturers such as Ford, Peugeot, Nissan, Vauxhall and Volkswagen – all have websites and have documentation available on their production methods.

Mountain bike

Introduction

Used by millions of people worldwide, the mountain bike is now the most popular bicycle in the Western world. Depending on the quality, mountain bike prices start at under £100 and rise to several thousands of pounds for top-of-the-range models.

Popular manufacturers of mountain bikes include Raleigh, Saracen, Orange, Marin and Claude-Butler.

Key parts

The key parts of a mountain bike include:

- frame and forks
- suspension
- handlebars and grips
- gearing
- wheels.

Key things to investigate
ICT

- CAD is often used in the design of mountain bikes to produce technical drawings of components and materials.
- CAM is used to help process the more intricate parts such as the gearing, etc.

- The manufacturers have websites to market, promote and sell their products.

- The manufacturing companies use a database to keep track of their employees, spare parts and bike models.

New materials and components
Mountain bikes consist of different materials and components designed to have specific properties such as good strength-to-weight ratios. Some of the key materials and components for investigation include:

- aluminium alloys and other metals used for the frame
- carbon and stainless steel used for gearing and brake cables
- fixtures such as various screws and bolts
- polymer materials used on the brakes, tyres and handle grips
- composite materials used for state-of-the-art wheels.

Systems and control technology
- In the larger manufacturers, state-of-the-art welding using TIG (tungsten inert gas shielding) and argon methods are automated to high quality standards.
- The painting process also utilises computer control technology to ensure an excellent finish.
- CNC is used to produce press tools and to carry out the final machining of components such as the gear spurs.

Where to look
Check out the websites shown opposite.

Saracen
www.saracen.co.uk

Orange
www.orange.co.uk

Raleigh
www.raleigh.co.uk

Marin
www.marin.co.uk

Shimano
www.shimano-europe.com/cycling/

case study

Electrical, electronic, telecommunications and computing

Portable CD player

Introduction
Becoming popular in the early 1990s, portable CD players allowed consumers to listen to digital music anytime, anywhere.

They are now extremely compact and lightweight, possess a high quality finish and can be purchased for a fraction of the original introductory price.

Popular manufacturers of these products include Sony, Sharp, Aiwa, Goodmans and Technics.

Key parts
The key parts of a portable CD player include:

* case and cover
* laser lens and pickup
* LCD display
* motor drive mechanism
* PCB
* headphones.

Key things to investigate
ICT

* CAD is used extensively in the design of CD players to produce all the technical drawings of components used on the PCB, drive mechanism and cover.
* CAE is used to help manufacture the parts using CAM and CNC. For example, the PCB is machined using a CNC milling machine and the plastic parts such as the

cover utilise CAE to machine the tools required for injection moulding.

- The manufacturers have websites to market, promote and sell their products.
- Companies use databases to keep track of their employees, spare parts and models.

New materials and components

- Investigate the properties of the glass fibre material used as the PCB base. Also on the PCB, examine the different components used, such as diodes, resistors and integrated circuits.
- Determine the polymer or metal material used as the cover for the CD player – ABS plastic and aluminium are often used.
- Investigate the LCDs – what are they made from, how do they work?
- Research the operation of a laser – how does it read the CD?

Systems and control technology

The manufacture of CD players is highly automated. Some key topics for investigation could include:

- the injection-moulding process used to manufacture the cover and other plastic parts
- surface-mount robotics used to place the tiny components into the exact position on the PCB
- conveyors and transfer machines required to handle parts and move materials between workstations in the factory
- how manual methods are integrated into the process using highly automated assembly procedures.

Where to look

- How Stuff Works (www.howstuffworks.com)
- Sony (www.sony.co.uk)
- Digital Recordings (www.digital-recordings.com)

Google search topics

- surface mount technology
- injection moulding
- PCB assembly
- CD player assembly

Exam hints

1 Read all the questions first and determine which carry the most marks and which questions you are confident in answering. With this in mind, attack these first, making sure you plan your time correctly and earn all the marks on offer.

2 Don't forget what is included in the three major categories of ICT, materials and components, and systems and control technology.

3 Read the questions carefully – a common mistake made by students is that a question may, for example, ask about control technology and the student's answer is about CAD – this is an example of ICT, not control technology. If the questions are asking about ICT/new materials/control technology, make sure your answers cover the relevant technologies within these categories – include as much information as you can, as long as it is relevant. To help you avoid misreading a question, underline the key words first, for example:

Describe <u>three advantages</u> of <u>control technology</u> used to make a <u>mobile phone</u>.

This should remind you of exactly what to include in your answer.

4 If the question is referring to a product, make sure you apply your answers to that product – try not to get sidetracked into discussing other examples.

5 Don't rush, and use all of your time to ensure you have answered the question fully and as best you can.

6 Think carefully about answering the question before you put pen to paper – use some scrap paper to jot down a few notes if necessary.

7 Write neatly and carefully; check your spelling and grammar.

Revision questions

1 Draw a line between the products shown below and their appropriate sector of manufacturing and engineering.

Mechanical/automotive

Engineering fabrication

Electrical/electronic/computer
  and telecommunications

Textiles and clothing

Printing and publishing/paper and board

Laptop computer

Mountain bike

Football boots

Shower gel

Audi TT

Hardback book

CD player

Bottle of cola drink

2 State an application of ICT in manufacturing and engineering.

3 State three benefits of CAD to a company.

4 State three disadvantages of CAD to a company.

5 Why is the Internet important to manufacturing and engineering companies?

6 How have robotics improved efficiency in the workplace?

7 What is a PLC and how is it used in industry?

8 State a traditional method of working in manufacturing and the technology that has replaced it.

9 What environmental consequences can result from poor manufacturing methods?

10 Has new technology affected the workforce in manufacturing and engineering?

Answers

Activity on page 6

Regulations	Legal obligations that the product must adhere to.
Scale of production	The size and amount of product being manufactured.
Maintenance	The capacity of a product to be serviced and repaired.
Performance	How well the product will do the intended task and how long it will last.
Intended market	The group of consumers for whom the design is being produced.
Function	What the product will be used for, who will use it and how.

Quiz on page 83

1 A design brief is a basic description of what the customer wants; a specification is a list of requirements in more practical detail
2 The customer
3 The parts of the design of major concern to the customer
4 So that it can be repaired, serviced and kept in good working order
5 Mass
6 Sir Isaac Newton
7 Forging
8 The appearance of a design
9 First and third angle
10 Computer aided design
11 An early working example of the finished product
12 This allows the trade of a product in the European Union.

Door handle activity on page 93

The main variations of the handle are as follows:

- colour
- size
- style.

The colour could be coded as – gold 'G', purple 'P' and red 'R'.

The size could be coded as large handles 'L' and small handles 'S'.

There are 3 main styles. 1,2 and 3 could suffice.

We will call the handle 'H' and add to it the description code.

This is one way of coding the components, but there is no correct way. You will probably have come up with a different system.

Activity on page 178

Print, Manufacturing, Ink, Substrate

Questions on page 225

One-fifth of one manager's time is spent on quality improvement:

one-fifth of £40 000 = £8000 (cost of prevention).

Half of quality assurance time is spent on inspection work:

half of £24 000 = £12 000 (cost of appraisal).

Half of maintenance time is spent dealing with breakdowns:

£42 000 × ½ = £21 000 (cost of internal failure).

One fifth of sales time is spent dealing with customer complaints:

one-fifth of £20 000 = £4000 (external failure).

One-fifth of finance spend time checking invoices for errors:

one-fifth of £25 000 is £5000 (cost of appraisal).

£50 000 a year in sales is lost to competitors:

£50 000 (lost opportunities).

The total cost of quality is therefore £100 000.

Activity on page 227

33 f s.

Questions on page 239

1 Excel;
2 the speed at which a product can be produced;
3 intermediate resource;
4 a quality standard;
5 packaging;
6 organisation chart;
7 verbal warning;
8 investment casting;
9 personal protective equipment;
10 No.

Index

accuracy, design requirements 8
acid rain 303
acrylic, properties 27
acrylonitrile-butadiene-styrene (ABS) 26, 278
action-oriented roles 125, 126
additives, papermaking 173
adhesives 30
Adobe InDesign 299
Adobe Photoshop 249
advertising x–xi
aesthetics
   and design 7, 8
   materials selection 22
agar medium 207
alloys 24, 275–6
aluminium 23
   alloys 275
analogue data 268
analysis techniques 8–9
anodes, diodes 282
appraisal costs 224
appraisals, performance 139
arbors 161
area charts, spreadsheets 262
arm and wrist robots 291
ARPANET (Advanced Research Projects Agency Network) 268
assembly, product
   drawings 43
   sequence 94
Association of the British Pharmaceutical Industry (ABPI) 206
attributive inspection 226–8
AutoCAD 2000 248
automated assembly robots 290
automated guided vehicles (AGVs) 289–90, 297
averages 235

bakelite 277
bar charts 231–2, 262
batteries 282–3
behaviour, safe 216
belt conveyors 288
bench drills 162
bench vices 163

Berners-Lee, Tim 268, 269
billets, defined 151
bills of materials (BOMs) 87
blanket-to-blanket presses 182
blending, tablet manufacture 209
blow moulding 153–4
board 23
boardstorming, see mind mapping
boots, safety 218
borders, drawings 58–9
bought-in parts 98, 140
brand analysis 199
brazing 29
British Printing Industries Federation 309
British Standards 51–3
   line types 70–1
button holes/ buttons, garments 202

cables, telecommunications 264
CAD, see computer-aided design (CAD)
CAE, see computer-aided engineering (CAE)
calendering, paper finishing 174
CAM, see computer-aided manufacturing (CAM)
capacitors 281
capacity, manufacturing 87
capital expenditure, paper industry 166
capital resources planning 97, 98
carding machines, cotton 194
case materials 169
casting
   metals processing 146–50
   plastics 153
cathodes, diodes 282
cause-effect diagrams 230
CD player, case study 316–17
CE marking 52
celluloid 277
central processing unit (CPU), PLCs 292
centre drills 163
centre lathes 156–9
centres of gravity 16–17

centrifugal casting 149
ceramics 23
   processing 154–5
cerebral roles 125, 126
charts 132
   quality control 228–9, 230–4
chemical pulp 170
chucks
   centre lathes 156–7
   drills 162
CIM, see computer-integrated manufacturing (CIM)
clay forming 154, 155
cleaning machines, cotton 194
client requirements, product specifications 8
clothing, coding 94
clothing manufacture 197–205
CMYK system 179–80
CNC, see computer numerical control (CNC)
co-ordinates, CAD systems 250
co-ordinators, people-oriented roles 126
CO_2 fire extinguishers 218
coated papers 167, 168
coated textiles, joining 205
coating agents, tablet manufacture 210
coating
   paper finishing 174
   tablet manufacture 210
coaxial cables 265
codes of conduct 135
coding systems 91–4
cold working, forming 151
colleagues, relationships 134
colour printing 179–80
command bar, CAD systems 251
committees 130
common impression cylinder presses 182
communication techniques 57, 129–33
compasses 61
competition, product specifications 7, 8
complaints 136

components 15–21, 281–6
  and production plans 94
  assembly 102
  bought-in 140
  code numbers 91–2
  information databases 89
  see also materials, new
composites 23, 279
compression moulding 153
compression, tablet manufacture 210
compressive force 17
computer numerical control (CNC) 254–6, 287–8
computer printers 189–90
computer-aided design (CAD) xi, 44, 81, 246, 248–53, 287–8
computer-aided engineering (CAE) 287–8, 293–4
computer-aided manufacturing (CAM) 144, 253–7, 287–8
computer-integrated manufacturing (CIM) 144, 287–8, 293–4
concept designs 38, 73, 78–9
concept boards 199
conflict management 137–8
constraints, design specifications 7
consumer testing 53
control systems, robots 291, 296
control technology xi, 302–3
Control of Substances Hazardous to Health (COSHH) 96, 100
conveyors 288–9, 297
copper 23
CorelDraw 249
corporate identity 198
correlation, defined 12
corrugated board 169
cost of quality 224–5
costs, and design 4, 5–6, 7, 40
cost estimating 54
cotton manufacture 194–5
counselling, employees 137
counter bores, drills 163
counter sinks, drills 163
crabbing, wool fabrics 194
creative roles 125, 126
crisps manufacture 213–15
criteria, design evaluation 39–40
critical operations 91
customers
  and ideas development 31
  and QFD 12
  databases 260

design specifications 7
  information from 8–9
  product specifications 8
cutting
  garments 202
  milling machines 159–62
cyclonic de-stoner 214
cylinder screen printing 187

dado joints 30
Data Protection Act 260
database management systems (DBMS) 259–60
databases 89, 258–61
de-inked pulp 170
de-inking, paper 176
deformation, components 17
density, to calculate 14–15
design, clothing 199
design briefs 4–6, 73, 77–8
design ideas development 31–55
design portfolios, completing 73–4
design specifications 7, 8, 40, 49–50, 73, 78
design stage 246
designs
  choice 49–50
  evaluation 39–40, 73
  modification 55
  presentation 56–73
  sketching 33, 34–7, 41
  testing 50–1, 53–4
desktop publishing software 249
despatch stage 247
diagrams, visual communication 132
die casting 148, 150
digital data 268
digital printing 189–90
diluents, tablet manufacture 210
dimensioning drawings 72–3
dimensions 13
  CAD systems 250
diodes 282
disciplinary procedures 134–6
discussions, verbal communication 132
disintegrants, tablet manufacture 210
dismissal 136
dispensing, tablet manufacture 209
display boards 74
displays, store 200

disposable materials 303–4
dividers 61
dot matrix printers 189
dovetail joints 30
drawing, glass 154
drawing (communication) 33, 34–7, 57, 132
  CAD systems 251
  equipment 60–1
  technical 41–4, 57–73, 75, 81, 82
drilling 159
  machines 162–3
drills, centre lathes 156
drugs development 207
drum plotters 190
dye sublimation printers 189
dying, wool 193

e-mail 131, 271–2
ear defenders, safety 218
ease of disposal, design specifications 7
electronic components 280–6
electronic/ electrical, computer/ telecommunications sector 244, 316–17
electronic mail, see e-mail
emergency stop buttons 216–17
employment opportunities loss 304–5
end effectors, robots 291
engineering fabrication, case study 314–15
engineering sectors 140, 244–6
engineering stages 246
environment
  design specifications 7
  materials selection 22
environmental impact 145, 303–4
epoxies 279
equipment
  life 95–6
  maintenance 221
  safety 138
  specification 95
erasers 60
ergonomics 7, 8
ethylene 278
European Standards 51–3
examination, see inspection
exceeded requirements costs 224
excipients, pharmaceutical preparations 208, 209–10

expendable mould casting 147–9
exploded drawings 44
exposure frame machines 299
external failure costs 224
extrusion 152
    plastics 153

fabrication equipment,
    maintenance 221
fabrication sector 244, 314–15
fabrics 191
    cotton 194–5
    joining processes 202–5
    selection 201
    synthetic 195–6, 196–7
    wool 191–4
facing off, lathe work 158
Fanuc 2000I robot 296
farads 281
fashion copywriting 199
fasteners 28–9
fatigue stress 277
fax 272–3
feedback cards 9
ferrous metals 23
fibre optic cables 265
fibre reinforced composites 279
fibres, paper 167
fields, databases 258
filler, non-fusion welding 29
fine liners 61
finish, design evaluation 40
finishers, roles 126
finishing 103, 247
    cotton 194
    wool 193
fire safety 218–20
fixtures specification 95
flat-bed screen printing 186
flatbed plotters 190
flexography 187–8
flow diagrams 230
foam fire extinguishers 218
focus groups 9
food and drink/ biological and
    chemical sector 242, 243
food and drink industry 212–15,
    310–11
food products, coding 93
forces
    magnifing 15, 18–19
    types 17–21
forest certification 171
forestry, and paper industry 170–2

Forestry Commission 171
forging 144, 151
form view, databases 259
forming 150–2
formulation, drugs 207–8
framed structures 21
friction 15, 19–20
fulcrums, see levers
fulling, wool fabrics 194
function
    and design briefs 4
    product specifications 8
fusion welding 29

antt charts 108, 109, 121
garments see clothing
gas emissions 303
gears, magnifing forces 15
general managers 114, 115, 123
glass processing 154–5
glassblowing 155
global warming 303
gloves, safety 218
goggles, safety 218
gold 24
granulation, tablet manufacture
    209, 210
graphical communication 57–82
graphics software 249
graphs 132
    quality control 228–9, 230,
    232–3
gravity conveyors 289
gravure printing 184–5
grid referencing systems, drawings
    59
grievance procedures 136–7

hand tools personnel 115, 116
hand-held vices 164
hardware, CAD systems 250
Hartlepool Mail 298–300
hazards, workshops 219
health and safety
    practice 138–9, 219–21
    resources planning 97, 99–100
    specifications 96
Health & Safety Executive (HSE)
    codes of practice 54
heatset printing 181
helmets, safety 218
hertz 266
highlighters 61
histograms 234

horizontal milling machines 161–2
hot working, forming 151
Hotmail, webmail 272
household papers 168
housekeeping, workplace 220–1
human resources planning 97, 98
hydroplastic forming 155
hypertext markup language' (HTML)
    268–9
hypertext transfer protocol (HTTP)
    268

ICT, see information and
    communications technology
    (ICT)
ideas
    development 31–55
    selecting 34, 38–40
illustrations 132
image carriers, printing 178, 184
image preparation, printing 179
image setting 299
impact printers 189
implementers, action-oriented roles
    126
industrial robots, see robots
information and communications
    technology (ICT) 301–2
    CD players 316–17
    food and drink industry 310
    manufacturing 248–73
    magazine production 308
    mountain bikes 314–5
    and MRP 88–91
    quality assurance 237, 238
    vehicle engines 312–13
infrastructure, communications 264
inhalation products, formulation
    208
injection moulding 25, 144, 153
injection products, formulation
    208
ink-jet printers 189
inks, printing 178, 183
inputs
    CAD 250
    CAM 257
    PLCs 292
inspection 225–8
    crisps manufacture 214
    criteria 106
    garments 203
    time 105
installation specifications 7

Institute of Operations Management 88
instructions 131
integrated circuits 285
integrated pulp 169
internal failure costs 224
internal memos 131
International Organisation for Standardisation (ISO) 100
Internet 267–71
   information from 9–10
Internet Protocol (IP) addresses 269
Internet Service Providers (ISPs) 269
intranets 271
inventory managers 114, 116
investment casting 148–9
iron 23
ISO 9000 100
isometric drawings 43, 66
IT, see information and communications technology (ICT)

jigs & fixtures specification 95
Johnston Press PLC 298–300
joining 28–30
journals, information from 10
Just in Time (JIT) systems 87–8

key features, and design choice 49–50
knurling 159
KP foods 213–15

lamps 283
landscape orientation 58
lap joints 30
laser printers 189
legality, design specifications 7
letterpress printing 183
letters 130
levers 15, 18–19
life of product, design specifications 7
life of service, design requirements 8
light-emitting diodes (LED) 282
line graphs 232–3, 262
line types, technical drawing 70–1
linings, garments 202
lithography 180–3
lockstitch flatbed sewing machines 204
lubricants, tablet manufacture 210
lubrication 20

machine finished paper 167
machine maintenance 221
   records 96
machine safety checks 96
machine tools 155–64
   maintenance 221
machine vices 159
machining robots 290
machinists 115, 116
magazine papers 167–8
magazines, information from 10
magnesium alloys 275
maintenance
   and design 4, 5, 7
   machines 96, 215, 221
   testing 53
malleability, defined 151
managers, production 114–15
manipulators, robots 291
manufacturing
   bought-in parts 141
   databases 260
   design criteria 7, 39–40, 80
   preparation for 139–41
   processes 94, 141–64, 246
   resource planning 86–8
manufacturing engineers, and QFD 12
manufacturing industry
   features xi
   managers 114, 115
   personnel planning 97, 98
   sectors 139–40, 242–3, 245–6
marker pens 61
market pulp 169
marketing 246–7
markets, and design 4, 5, 7, 8
marking out
   garments 202
   personnel 115, 116
masks, safety 218
mass, product 14
materials
   handling 288–91
      moving time 105, 107–8
      robots 290
   new 273–80, 302, 306, 309, 311, 313, 315, 317
   processing 102, 142–3
      preparation 101–2, 140
      joining 28–30, 202–5
   properties 22, 53, 142–3, 172
   resource planning 97, 98–9

materials requirement
   planning (MRP) 87
   ordering 110–11
   supply and control stage 247
   usage calculations 110
safety 138
   COSHH checks 96
selection 22–9, 280
   and design 7, 8, 40, 79–80
   specification 94
   testing 53
mean averages 235–6
measuring equipment 100
mechanical/ automotive sector 244, 312–13
mechanical pulp, paper 167, 170
median averages 235
meetings, minutes 115–16, 130
metals 23–4, 27, 146, 274–6
   processing 145–52
   selection table 27
Microsoft Access 89, 260
Microsoft Excel 90, 261
Microsoft Project 90–1
milling machines 159–62, 255
milling vices 164
mind mapping 32–3, 229
minutes, meetings 115–16, 130
mirror images, printing 178
misconduct 134–5
mitre joints 30
mode averages 235
modelling 44, 45–6, 81
models
   CAM 256
   changes in 11
   design portfolio 73
   presentation 75
modems 268
modification notes, design portfolio 73
monitors/ evaluators, cerebral roles 127
monomers 278
mood boards 74
morse tapers, drills 162
mortise and tenon joints 30
motivation 128, 133
motors 284
moulding, plastics 152–3
mountain bike, case study 314–15
MSN Messenger 131
music, communication aids 133

nails 30
National Health Service (NHS) 206
negotiation, conflict management 138
newspaper production 298–300
newsprint 167
nickel-based alloys 275
Nissan UK 295–7
non-active ingredients, pharmaceutical preparations 208, 209–10
non-critical operations 91
non-ferrous metals 23–4
non-fusion welding 29
non-heatset printing 181
non-sterile products manufacture 210
non-verbal communication 57
notice boards, visual communication 132
numerical control (NC) 254–6
nylon 278
  fabrics 195–6
  wear resistance 27

oblique projections 43, 67
offset lithographic printing 180–3
ohms 281
online communication 131
operating environment, and design 8
operation time 104, 108–9
opportunity costs 224
optical fibre cables 265
oral presentations 75
oral products, formulation 208
organisation charts 113–17
organisational policy, breaches 139
orthographic projections 41–2, 67–70, 81, 82
outputs
  CAD 250
  CAM 257
  PLCs 293
overalls, safety 218
overhead conveyors 289, 298
ozone layer depletion 303

packaging 7, 103, 187, 215
packing stage 247
pad printing 190
paints 61
paper 23, 166
  coding 94

sizes 58
types 167
packaging 169
paper industry 165–76
paper machines 173–4
parallel turning 157
parent reel stock, paper 168
parting off, lathe work 157
parts
  code numbers 91–2
  and production plans 94
patents, design specifications 7
patterns
  casting 147–8
  fabrics 200
  garments 201
pencil grades 60
penicillin, discovery 206–7
people-oriented roles 125, 126
performance appraisals 139
performance
  and design 4, 5, 7
  testing 53
permanent mould casting 149–50
personal protective equipment (PPE) 96, 218
personnel
  checks, H&S 96
  documentation 118
  see also teams
personnel managers 115, 116
perspective drawings 62–5
pharmaceutical industry 206–11
photochromic materials 276
photographs, visual communication 132
physical characteristics, design requirements 8
picking machines, cotton 194
pictorial drawings 42–3
pie charts 232, 262
piezoelectric materials 276–7
pillar drills 162
pivots, see levers
planning and scheduling case study 112–23
plants, cerebral roles 127
plastics, see polymers
plate preparation, printing 184
plateless print processes 188–90
platens, printing 184
platinum 24
playback control systems, robots 291

plotters 189–90
pocket making, garments 202
politics, design specifications 7
pollution 303
polycarbonate 278
polyesters 196–7, 278
polyethylene 152, 278
polyethylene terephthalate (PET) 196–7
polymers 25–7, 152–4, 277–9
polypropylene processing 152
polystyrene 26, 152, 278
polyvinyl chloride (PVC) 26, 152, 278
portrait orientation 58
posters, visual communication 132
potatoes, crisps manufacture 213–15
powder fire extinguishers 218
power supply, robots 291
PowerPoint presentations 75–6, 133
precious metals 24
presentation software 133
presentation techniques 74–6, 77–82
presses, see printing presses
pressing
  garments 202, 203
  glass 154
prevention costs 224
price, and bought-in parts 140
price sensitivity 6
printed circuits boards (PCBs) 285–6
printing and publishing industry 177–90, 308–9
printing/ publishing/ paper/ board sector 242
printing
  fabrics 200
  paper 168
  presses, 221, 298–300
  process 177
Pro Engineer 248
process checks, risk assessment 96
processing 141–2, 247
  control techniques 225–37
  costs 143
  design specifications 7
  selection criteria 142–5
  times 96, 104–5
procurement, defined 86–7
product art direction 199

product databases 89, 260
product life 11
production
  characteristics 8
  control techniques 221–38
  documentation 117–23
  methods 4, 5
    evaluating 53–4
  planning 90–100, 113, 247
  process specification 95
  roles 114–15
  scale 54–5
  scheduling 101–11, 121
  sequence specification 94
  stages 101–5, 246
production engineers 215
production managers 114, 116, 121–2
products
  characteristics 143
  codes 91–4
  inspection 97
  investigation 12
  physical properties 12–13
  specifications 8–11, 112
  testing 50–1, 53–4
profile cutting 160
programmable logic controllers (PLCs) 292–3
project diaries 73
project planning software 90–1
proofs, printing 182
prototypes
  design portfolio 73
  evaluation 48–50
  modelling, design case study 81–2
  presentation 75
  testing 48
prototyping 46–50
Provision & Use of Work Equipment Regulations (PUWER) 100
pulp, paper industry 169–70, 173

quality
  checks 96–7
  and design 7, 40
  managers 114, 116
  and processing 144
  resources planning 97, 100
  standards 4–5, 100
  systems 100
quality assurance 224, 263–4

quality control 117, 202, 215, 221–38
quality costs 223–5
quality function deployment (QFD) 12
quantity 7, 8
  and processing 144
questionnaires, marketing 8
queuing time 105, 107–8

radio waves 265–7
rapid prototyping 47–8, 81–2
raw materials 98, 101–2
records, databases 258
recycling
  fabrics 197
  materials 99, 303–4, 311
  paper 168, 173, 175–6
refractory materials 147
regulations
  and design briefs 4, 6
  business 54
reinforced plastics 279
reliability, and design 7, 8
remotely operated vehicles (ROVs) 289–90
renderings, design 199
research notes, design portfolio 73
research techniques, for design 8–9
resistors 281
resource investigators 126
resource requirements planning 97–123
responsibilities allocation 124–5
retail store planning 200
rewards 118
risk assessment
  process checks 96
  workshops 217, 219
rivets 29
robot vehicles 289–90, 297
robotics xi, 289–90, 290–3, 295–7
  employment opportunities loss 304–5
roles, production 114–15
roller conveyors 289
rolling, forming 151
rotary webfed letterpresses 184
rotation, centres of gravity 16–17
rotational moulding, plastics 153
rotogravure printing 184–5
rules (rulers), measurement 60

safety
  and design 7, 8
  documentation 119
  equipment 96
  managers 114, 116
sand casting 147–8
sanitary papers 168
scale of production, and design briefs 4, 6
scatter diagrams 233–4, 262
scatter measurement 236
scheduling case study 112–23
screen printing 185–7
seams, garments 202, 203
security, workplace 138
semi-chemical pulp 170
service
  materials selection 22
  resources planning 97, 99
set squares 60
set-up time 104, 108
sewing 30
  garments 202, 203
sewing machines, industrial 204–5, 221
shape memory alloys 277
shapers, action-oriented roles 126
shear force 17
shearing, sheep 192
sheet metal forming 152
sheetfed presses 181, 184
shelf life, design requirements 8
shell-mould casting 149
shipping, design specifications 7
silicone 278
silk fabrics 196
silver 24
six sigma quality 222
size
  design specifications 4, 5, 7, 8, 80–1
  testing 53
sketches 33, 34–7, 132
  see also drawing
slat conveyors 288
slip casting 155
slitting, paper finishing 174
smart materials xi, 276
soldering 29
solid structures 21
sorting and grading, wool 193
sound, communication 133
spare parts databases 261
specialised papers 169

specialists, cerebral roles 127
spinning 191, 193, 194
sports sponsorship x–xi
spot faces, drills 163
spot prints, fabrics 200
spot welding robots 290, 296
spray painting robots 290
spreadsheets 90, 261–4
squashed material, compressive
    force 17
stainless steel 276
standard deviation 236
standards 7, 51–3
statistical process control (SPC)
    233
statistics, quality assurance 234–7
steel 23
    see also alloys
stencils 61
stereo-lithography (STL), rapid
    prototyping 81–2
sterile products manufacture 211
stitching, joining 30
stock
    availability 110
    control documentation 120
stockholding, and bought-in parts
    141
stresses 277
stretching, components 17
structures, resistance 15, 20–1
sub-assemblies 91
substrates, printing 177, 179
supervision, workshops 217
supplier information databases 89
symbols
    charts 231
    circuits 281–3
synthetic fabrics 195–6, 196–7
systems and control technology
    287–300, 306, 309, 311, 313,
    315, 317

T-squares 60–1
tables, spreadsheets 262
tablets, manufacture 209–11
tailstock, centre lathes 156
taper turning 158
target product cost, production
    characteristics 8
target setting 128
tasks allocation 124–5, 128

teams
    building 124–39
    meeting minutes 115–16
    roles 124, 125–7
    teamwork 124–39
technical drawing 41–4, 57–73, 75,
    81, 82
telecommunications 264–73
telephones, verbal communication
    132
templates 61
tensile force 17
textbooks, information from 10
textile industry 23, 191–205
textiles and clothing sector 242,
    306–7
texting, phone 131
thermochromic materials 276
thermoplastics 26, 278
    processing 152
    selection table 28
thermoset plastics 26, 278
    processing 152
threaded fasteners 28–9
three-dimensional modelling (CAD)
    44, 81
titanium alloys 275
title blocks, drawings 58–9
tongue and groove joints 30
tooling
    life 95–6
    maintenance 221
    resources planning 97, 99
    specification 95
topical products, formulation 208
torsional force 17
total quality management (TQM)
    223
training shoes case study 306–7
transfer pad printing 190
transformers 284
transistors 284
trees, for paper making 171–2
turning operations, lathe 156–9
turnover, manufacturing/
    engineering sectors 245–6
twist drills 162

UK Woodland Assurance
    Standard (UKWAS) 171
uniform resource locators (URLs)
    269

unit-design presses 182
UV curing systems, printing 186

value engineering 48–50
variable inspection 226
variable resistors 283
variation measurement 236
vehicles
    engines 312–13
    robot 289–90, 297
verbal communication 57, 129,
    131–2
verbal warnings 135
vertical milling machines 160
virgin pulp, paper 168
visual communication 129, 132–3
volume, product 14, 80–1

warnings 135
waste materials disposal 303–4
water fire extinguishers 218
web-fed presses, lithography 181
webmail 272
webs, paper 166
websites 132, 269–71
weighing heads, crisps manufacture
    215
weight, product 8, 14
welding 29, 205
wire 283
wood 23
    joints 30
    paper making 171–2
    selection table 28
wool manufacture 191–4
work holding devices 163–4
working environment 134
working relationships 134, 139
worksheets, spreadsheets 261
workshops
    health and safety 216–21
    personnel 217
World Wide Web 267–71
wrapping, paper finishing 174
writing paper 168
written communication 129,
    130–1
written warnings 135

Yahoo Messenger 131
yarns 191, 193, 194